THE
Ultimate TRIVIA
Quiz
BOOK

Over 3000 brain teasers to challenge all the family

Compiled by Joyce Robins

PARRAGON

First published in Great Britain in 1994 by
Parragon.
13, Whiteladies Road
Clifton
Bristol BS8 1PB

This edition published in 1998
Reprinted in 1999

ISBN 0 75252 448 8

Printed in India

Editorial: Linda Doeser Publishing Services
Design Style: David Rowley Design
Design and DTP: David Rowley and Alan Mckee
Picture Research: Kathy Lockley

Contents

Introd

There are over 100 quizzes in this book to amuse, perplex, absorb and even educate you. Most of us carry far more general knowledge in our heads than we realize. The only problem is tracking down the trivia at the right moment and producing a prompt answer. It can be satisfying and frustrating by turns, but it is always fun.

Some questions are so easy that you will hardly have to think; others will leave you cudgelling your brains. But then, of course, the only way quiz addicts will define an easy question is one where they know the answer. Some readers will romp through the intricacies of American football or Olympic competition, while others find musical

uction

shows or cocktail ingredients more to their taste. In Pot Luck, everyone has an equal chance.

Quizzes are fun for the whole family and if you find the names of dinosaurs impossible to pronounce – let alone remember – just ask your children. The chances are they will be able to answer every question!

Whether you use this book to give your brain a gentle workout or stage a full-scale family-and-friends competition, it will give you many hours of entertainment and you will end up knowing more than when you started.

How to play

There is no 'right' way to play Ultimate Trivia. You can make up your own rules, or simply dip into the book for fun, but we have devised a few games to help you make the most of the 350 questions in each subject category.

Game 1: Single player

Pick your favourite from the seven subject categories (not including Pot Luck) and try to answer each question in order, scoring 1 point for each correct answer. Every time you fail to answer, take a question from Pot Luck 1. If you answer correctly, score 2 points, if not, deduct 1 point from your current score. When you have exhausted the questions in Pot Luck 1, the game is over. Next time you can begin again from where you left off, using Pot Luck 2, and competing against your last score.

Game 2: 2 or more players or teams

Each player or team picks a subject, which can include Pot Luck. You can cut cards or throw dice to decide who chooses first - or you can make the game more difficult by putting all the categories in a hat and making a random choice. Decide in advance how long you want the game to last, then go through the book with each player or team taking turns to answer question 1 in their chosen category, then question 2. Score 2 points for each correct answer. The winner is the person or team with most points when time is up. For the next round, start again where you left off.

Game 3: Several teams with 3 or more members, and a quiz master

Put numbers from 1 to 25 in a hat. Each team draws a number and tries to answer that number in one quiz after another each time their turn comes round. The questions aren't graded for difficulty, so no team is at a disadvantage and team members can confer over their answers. Each correct answer in the subject categories earns 1 point but each time a Pot Luck question is answered correctly, the team score is doubled. The game can be played again with each team drawing a second number and proceeding through the book in the same way.

1. King Edward VIII gave up the British throne to marry an American divorcée. What was her name? ▶

2. Whom did filmstar Grace Kelly marry in 1956? ▶

3. Queen Victoria proposed marriage to her cousin Prince Albert at Windsor in 1839. What nationality was he?

4. Who married Robert Browning at a London church, in the utmost secrecy, because her father disapproved of the match?

5. Elizabeth Taylor and Richard Burton fell passionately in love when they were filming a motion picture epic. What was the film?

6. Who was known as the cinema screen's first 'great lover', star of The Sheikh?

7. Lauren Bacall and Humphrey Bogart were known as a devoted couple. Her friends have always called her by her given name, rather than by the glamorous 'Lauren'. What is that name?

8. The close relationship between Spencer Tracy and Katherine Hepburn lasted 25 years. In 1967 they made their last film together, Guess Who's Coming to Dinner. Who was coming to dinner?

9. The man reputed to be the greatest lover of all time lived in the 18th century and his name has passed into the language. Who was he?

10. Who was the love of the Emperor Napoleon's life?

11. Which two royal lovers, parents of the young Princes William and Henry, announced their separation in 1992?

12. When Lord Nelson died, one of his last requests was 'Take care of my dear Lady Hamilton'. What was her first name?

13 Who did assasinated president John F. Kennedy's widow marry in 1968?

14 Which film actress fed her image as a blonde sex symbol with lines like 'Come up and see me sometime,' and 'I never set out to make men a career. It just happened that way!'?

15 Nell Gwyn won the heart of England's 'Merry Monarch'. Who was he?

16 Which of Henry VIII's wives died soon after the birth of her baby while she was still the object of the king's love?

17 Both Julius Caesar and Mark Antony loved Cleopatra. When she ascended the throne she was formally married to a relative. Who was he?

18 What is the name of the village in Scotland where runaway English couples were once married over the blacksmith's anvil?

19 Who is the patron saint of lovers?

20 Name the well-known singer who is Andrew Lloyd Webber's second wife, and who starred in Phantom of the Opera.

21 Of which French king was Madame de Pompadour the influential mistress ?

22 Which group of people were associated with the saying 'Make love, not war'?

23 Which world famous baseball star married Marilyn Monroe in 1954?

24 Winston Churchill married in 1908 and wrote that he and his wife 'lived happily ever after'. What was her Christian name?

25 Mary Queen of Scots supposedly wrote the 'Casket Letters' to her lover with whom she plotted to kill her husband. Name the recipient of the letters.

1. At the climax of North by Northwest, the hero and heroine climb across the faces of American presidents on a famous monument. Name it.

2. Barbara Bel Geddes played James Stewart's down-to-earth girlfriend in Vertigo in 1958. In what television role did she become famous more recently?

3. Who stars opposite Ingrid Bergman as an American agent in Notorious?

4. In Rebecca, Laurence Olivier marries Joan Fontaine and brings her back to his family home in Cornwall. What is the name of his imposing house? ▼

5. Who plays the title role in Rebecca?

6. What nationality was Alfred Hitchcock? ▶

7. Which film has a sequel in which Norman Bates is released from a mental institution?

8. Marnie is the story of a compulsive thief based on a novel by which author?

9. In which country does the action of To Catch a Thief, starring Cary Grant and Grace Kelly, take place?

56

10 In Rear Window , James Stewart plays a news photographer who believes he has witnessed a murder from his window. Why is he confined to his apartment?

11 In an early film, Shadow of a Doubt , Joseph Cotton plays Uncle Charlie, who moves in with his sister and niece, who was named after him. Gradually his niece becomes suspicious of him. What is his guilty secret?

12 Margaret Lockwood is perplexed by the disappearance of an elderly English governess in The Lady Vanishes. Where does the action of the film take place?

13 Jessica Tandy played the hero's mother in The Birds. For which film did the elderly actress win an academy award in 1989?

14 In Spellbound, Gregory Peck suffers from amnesia and fears that he is a murderer. The character played by Ingrid Bergman tries to help him. What is her profession?

15 Jamaica Inn was taken from a novel by a well-known English author. Name her.

16 What was Hitchcock's last film, made in 1976?

17 In Rope, two young men commit murder for the thrill of it and then hold a party, serving food from the chest which contains the body. Who plays the college professor who discovers their secret?

18 Hitchcock freely adapted John Buchan's novel for his film The Thirty-Nine Steps. What are the Thirty-Nine Steps?

19 In Strangers on a Train , Bruno (Robert Walker) believes he has made a bargain with Guy (Farley Granger) whereby Guy is to kill Bruno's father. What does Bruno do for Guy?

20 In Psycho, the first victim is killed in a motel. What is she doing at the time?

21 The crash of a fairground ride provides the climax in Strangers on a Train. Which ride is it?

22 Complete the following Hitchcock quotation. 'The length of the film should be directly related to the endurance of ...'.

23 Hitchcock made two films of the same name and with virtually the same story in 1935 and 1956, the second starring James Stewart and Doris Day. Name the film.

24 From 1955 to 1961 Hitchcock introduced a series of mystery stories on television. What was the series called?

25 Which star do The Birds and Marnie have in common?

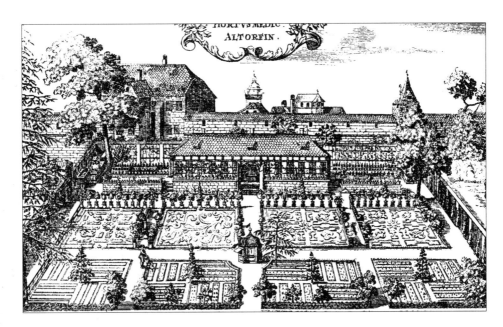

1 In Shakespeare's Hamlet, which herb is said to be 'for remembrance'?

2 Is parsley an annual, biennial or perennial plant?

3 Is French or Russian tarragon normally used in cooking?

4 In which two European countries is caraway often used to flavour breads and pastries?

5 What is the main problem with growing mint in the garden? ▲

6 From which flower does the expensive spice of saffron come?

7 Which of the following plants are hardy annuals: sage, borage, chives, sorrel, dill?

8 In what form is angelica normally used for decorating cakes and desserts?

9 The traditional French blend of 'fines herbes' includes chervil, chives and tarragon. What is the fourth herb?

10 Which herb was regarded as a symbol of immortality by the Greeks and Romans?

11 Fresh coriander leaves are used in Indian cookery and the rest of the plant can also be cooked and eaten. Which vegetable family does it belong to?

12 Which herb is used to flavour the tomato-based sauce on pizza?

13 Sage is now a familiar herb in the kitchen. What was its main purpose in the Middle Ages?

14 Which is milder: American mustard or Dijon mustard?

15 With which of type dish would you use lemon balm as a flavouring?

16 What type of soil does thyme prefer?

17 In the Middle East, cardamom is used in coffee and in Europe it flavours cakes. In France and the United States, its oil is used for a purpose unconnected with cookery. What is it?

18 With what type of food are juniper berries most often used?

19 Which part of the ginger plant does the spice come from? ▼

20 What is a mixture of dried thyme, bay and parsley enclosed in a muslin bag called?

21 Which herb sends cats into ecstasies?

22 What type of flavour does the vegetable fennel have?

23 Camomile is often used in herbal tea. What is it said to promote?

24 The curry plant has a very spicy aroma and silver leaves. What colour are the flowers of the plant?

25 Which of the following is not a herb or spice: savory, soapwort, soy, sassafras?

1 On a darts board, what number is directly opposite No. 1?

2 What colour is the cue ball in pool?

3 What is the craft of making arrows called?

4 In cycle racing, what is a sag wagon?

5 The apparatus used by male gymnasts consists of vaulting horse, pommel horse, horizontal bars, rings and floor. Which of these pieces of apparatus do women use?

6 Essential equipment for a boxer comprises gloves, hand tape, protector below the waist, boots and – what else?

7 Why do American footballers paint black marks across their cheeks? ◀

8 In ice hockey, what are puck-stoppers?

9 In the early days of cricket, a bowler who took three wickets in a row was presented with a top hat. What modern term comes from this practice?

10 What sport has four different colour codes for the balls, ranging from yellow for hot conditions to blue for cold conditions?

11 Apart from body padding, what protection do baseball players wear?

12 In hot air ballooning, how is the manoeuvring or cooling valve used? ▶

13 How many red balls are there in snooker?

14 Which sport uses stones and a house?

15 Starting blocks are used on athletic tracks. Runners push their feet against them to get the fastest start possible. What else can they be used for?

16 In fencing, which is the heavier weapon: the foil or the épée?

17 What is the difference in shape between rugby and soccer balls?

18 Kendo is one of the traditional Japanese martial arts and the participants use a type of sword. From what is the sword made?

19 What type of shots are woods used for in golf?

20 What colour is the centre scoring zone of an archery target?

21 All the hoops in croquet are painted white, except the last one, called the rover, which has a different colour on the crown. Which colour is it?

22 Why are the officials in American football known as zebras?

23 From what fairly light-weight wood is a bat for the sport of cricket traditionally made from?

24 In the ancient sport of archery, what material are the arrows usually made from?

25 Soccer boots have interchangeable studs. The studs for wet and slippery surfaces are made from aluminium. What studs are used for playing on hard ground?

1 Where did the Great Fire of London break out in 1666?

2 Where was the Piper Alpha oil rig belonging to the U.S. Occidental Petroleum Corporation, which exploded in 1988?

3 One of the worst fires in American history gutted the 26-storey MGM Grand Hotel in 1980. In which town was the hotel situated?

4 The ancient Italian town of Pompeii and a great number of its inhabitants were buried when a volcano near Naples erupted in 79AD. Name the great volcano, which is now a tourist attraction.

5 Who was the tyrant leader of the Khymer Rouge whose reign of terror killed some 3 million people in Cambodia in the 1970s?

6 In 1989, the Chinese People's Liberation Army crushed a student pro-democracy protest in Beijing with tanks and machine-gun fire. In which large square did the massacre take place?

7 Which geological fault caused the San Francisco earthquake of 1906?

8 The Welsh mining village of Aberfan suffered a major disaster in 1966 when 81 schoolchildren died. What caused the tragedy?

9 In the 14th century, a plague killed up to one third of Europe's population. What was it called?

10 Both the Hindenburg and the R101 ended in flames. What were they?

11 What is measured on the Richter scale?

12 Which American river caused serious flood damage in 1993?

13 How many voyages had the Titanic made when it hit an iceberg and sank in 1912? ▲▶

14 A Pan Am flight, which left London Heathrow bound for New York in December 1988, was blown up by a bomb over a small Scottish town. Name the town.

15 What was Krakatoa?

16 What type of accident happened at Chernobyl in the U.S.S.R. in 1986?

17 Which three sectarian groups are involved in the conflict in Bosnia and Herzogovina?

18 Name the American space shuttle, its crew including a teacher (the first private citizen chosen for a space mission), which exploded killing all on board after lift-off?

19 What is the name given to those who study and predict earthquakes?

20 AIDS has become a worldwide health problem. What do the initials stand for?

21 The American volcano of Mount St. Helens erupted in May 1980. In which state is the volcano?

22 Which Indian city suffered a large death toll after a chemical leak at the Union Carbide (India) factory in December 1984?

23 The worst oil spill ever known in the United States occurred when the Exxon Valdez ran aground. Where did the spill occur?

24 In the 1960s, a tranquillizing drug, thought to have no harmful side effects, was marketed in Britain and other countries as a therapy for morning sickness, resulting in the birth of hundreds of deformed babies. Name the drug.

25 What are the scientists who study volcanoes called?

1 The name 'dinosaur' comes from two Greek words. What do they mean?

2 How long did dinosaurs live on earth?

3 What was remarkable about the fast-running predator the Compsognathos?

4 The dinosaur once known as the Brontosaurus is now known by another name. What is it?

5 The Euoplocephalus had a bony protective layer over its body. What did it have at the end of its tail?

6 Researchers think that the Diplodocus, the longest land animal known, suffered from a painful disease that often affects humans as they grow older. What was it?

7 Why was the Stegasaurus, or 'roofed lizard' so called?

8 What was remarkable about the brain of the Stegosaurus?

9 Was the Brachiosaurus the fastest or slowest of the dinosaurs?

10 Why was the Iguanodon able to use its forefeet as a weapons?

11 What did the Spinosaurus have on its back, which may have played a part in heat regulation?

12 Which was the largest carnivore ever known on earth?

13 What does the name Triceratops mean?

14 Which London park contains models of dinosaurs created by Benjamin Waterhouse Hawkins in the last century?

15 Dinosaurs divide into two main classes: Saurischia and Ornithischia. The Saurischia were lizard-hipped, much like other reptiles. What were the Ornithischia?

16 How did dinosaurs produce their young?

17 In 1960 Irwin Allen directed The Lost World, in which a party of scientists encountered living dinosaurs. Which author wrote the book on which the film was based? ◀

18 The Chinese call fossilized dinosaur teeth 'dragon's teeth'. What are they used for?

19 What ability did the duck-billed dinosaurs share with modern-day hamsters?

20 The name Deinonychus reflects the ability of this fierce flesh-eater to overcome its prey with a large, sickle-like claw on its inner toe. What does the name mean?

21 What are the scientists who study dinosaur fossils called? ▲

22 The first skeleton of the Archaeopteryx or 'ancient wing' was found in Germany in 1861. What is its claim to fame?

23 In the film Jurassic Park, how were the dinosaurs supposed to have been created?

24 Dinosaurs lived in the Mesozoic Era, which is divided into three periods. Two of them are the Jurassic and Cretaceous. What is the third? ▼

25 How long ago did dinosaurs die out?

7 Who was the first woman President of Israel?

8 Who said, 'Je suis la France'?

9 What was British Prime Minister Margaret Thatcher's maiden name? ▼

10 Which Iraqi leader ordered the invasion of Kuwait?

11 Which musical instrument does President Bill Clinton play?

12 By what name was Indian political leader Mohandas Gandhi better known?

13 Who declared war on Britain and France in June 1940?

1 What was the nationality of Adolf Hitler? ▲

2 Which American President ordered the dropping of the first atomic bomb?

3 Who wrote his thoughts in a little red book?

4 Who has been in power in Cuba since declaring the country a socialist nation over 30 years ago?

5 Which British Prime Minister said, 'You've never had it so good' and spoke of the 'wind of change'?

6 Where did the burglary that led to the resignation of an American President take place?

14 What was the slogan of Martin Luther King's famous speech made at the Lincoln Memorial, Washington in 1963 in which he looked forward to understanding between races? ▲

15 Which African leader emerged from prison after 27 years to lead his party again?

16 Which President of the Soviet Union died in 1953, aged 73?

17 What political position did Ronald Reagan hold before becoming President of the United States?

18 Which wartime leader said. 'Never in the field of human conflict was so much owed by so many to so few'?

19 By what military rank is the President of Libya known?

20 Ceylon (now Sri Lanka) had the first female head of government in the modern world when she succeeded her husband after his assassination in 1959. What was her name?

21 In 1941, the Deputy Chancellor of Germany flew to Britain to try to sue for peace. He was later imprisoned in Spandau prison. Who was he?

22 Richard M. Nixon was President of the United States from 1969 to 1974. What does M. stand for?

23 Which Third World leader was assassinated by members of her bodyguard in 1984?

24 Which Russian leader introduced glasnost and perestroika ?

25 Which British Prime Minister said, 'A week is a long time in politics'?

1 Where in the body is the labyrinth?

2 What is the common name for ascorbic acid?

3 Complete this quotation from Voltaire: 'If god did not exist ...'.

4 Americans call it a faucet. What do the British call it?

5 How are the first five books of the Bible known collectively?

6 Who designed the dome of St. Peter's, Rome? ▲

7 What is the unit of currency in Poland?

8 Which two elements make up water?

9 Who was the captain of the Pequod in Moby Dick?

10 What colour is a New York taxi?

11 Which two letters are worth 10 points in the board game Scrabble?

12 Which useful household item is made from naphthalene?

13 What is measured on the Beaufort scale?

14 Which creatures live in a formicary?

15 Which bandleader died in an air crash over the English Channel during World War II?

16 What is the other name for the Jewish Day of Atonement?

17 What was writer Charles Dodgson's pseudonym?

18 If an American footballer talked about his 'zippers' what would he mean?

19 Where would you find the 'ocean of storms'?

20 What is the pirate's flag with the skull and cross-bones called?

21 Where is the original Harris tweed spun and woven?

22 What do climbers call a peak higher than 914 m (3,000 ft)?

23 The famous Gurkha soldiers are known for carrying a particular type of large knife. What is this knife called?

24 Which bird is the international symbol of happiness?

25 What is the centuries old art of clipping hedges into various ornamental shapes traditionally called? ▼

TOPIARY WORK AT LEVENS HALL : WESTMORELAND

People and Places Lovers

1. Wallis Simpson
2. Prince Rainier of Monaco
3. German
4. Elizabeth Barrett
5. Cleopatra
6. Rudolph Valentino
7. Betty
8. Their daughter's black fiancé
9. Casanova
10. Josephine
11. The Prince and Princess of Wales
12. Emma
13. Aristotle Onassis
14. Mae West
15. Charles II
16. Jane Seymour
17. Her brother, Ptolemy
18. Gretna Green
19. Saint Valentine
20. Sarah Brightman
21. Louis XV
22. Hippies
23. Joe DiMaggio
24. Clementine
25. Earl of Bothwell

Entertaining Arts Hitchcock Films

1. Mount Rushmore
2. Miss Ellie in Dallas
3. Cary Grant
4. Manderley
5. No one. Rebecca is already dead when the story opens.
6. English
7. Psycho
8. Winston Graham
9. France
10. He has a broken leg
11. He murders rich widows
12. On a train
13. Driving Miss Daisy
14. Psychiatrist
15. Daphne du Maurier
16. The Family Plot
17. James Stewart
18. A ring of spies
19. Kills his wife
20. Taking a shower
21. The carousel
22. '... the human bladder'
23. The Man Who Knew Too Much
24. Alfred Hitchcock Presents
25. Tippi Hedren

Food and Drink Herbs and Spices

1. Rosemary
2. Biennial
3. French
4. Germany and Austria
5. It spreads rapidly
6. Crocus
7. Borage and dill
8. Crystallized
9. Parsley
10. Tansy
11. Carrot family
12. Oregano
13. Medicinal
14. American
15. Fish and poultry
16. Well-drained lime or chalk
17. Game
18. The underground rhizome
20. Bouquet garni
21. Catnip or catmint
22. Aniseed
23. Relaxation and sleep
24. Yellow
25. Soy is a condiment made from fermented soya beans

Sports and Pastimes Sports Gear

1. No. 19
2. White
3. Fletching
4. One of the last vehicles following road events and picking up riders who have dropped out
5. Vaulting horse and floor
6. Gumshield
7. It helps protect against the sun's glare
8. Pads protecting knees and shins
9. Hat-trick
10. Squash
11. Helmet and face-mask
12. To release hot air for descent
13. 15
14. Curling
15. To detect false starts
16. The épée
17. A rugby ball is oval; a soccer ball is round
18. Strips of bamboo
19. Long shots
20. Gold
21. Red
22. They wear striped shirts
23. Willow
24. Tubular aluminium alloy
25. Rubber studs

History Catastrophe!

1. A baker's shop in Pudding Lane
2. North Sea
3. Las Vegas
4. Vesuvius
5. Pol Pot
6. Tiananmen Square
7. San Andreas Fault
8. A slag heap (mine waste) collapsed
9. Black Death
10. Airships
11. Earthquakes
12. Mississippi
13. None; it was her maiden voyage
14. Lockerbie
15. A volcanic island
16. A nuclear reactor caught fire
17. Serbs, Croats and Muslims
18. Challenger
19. Seismologists
20. Acquired immune deficiency syndrome
21. Washington
22. Bhopal
23. Alaska
24. Thalidomide
25. Volcanologists

Natural World Dinosaurs

1. Terrible lizard
2. 150 million years
3. It was the smallest known
4. Apatosaurus
5. A large lump of bone with which it could club its enemies
6. Arthritis
7. The bony plates on its back looked like roof tiles
8. It was tiny in relation to the creature's size
9. Slowest
10. Its thumbs formed powerful spikes
11. A tall fin
12. Tyrannosaurus rex
13. Three-horned face
14. Crystal Palace
15. Bird-hipped
16. They laid eggs in hollowed-out nests in the ground
17. Sir Arthur Conan Doyle
18. Medicines
19. They could store extra food in their cheeks
20. Terrible claw
21. Palaeontologists
22. It was probably the earliest bird
23. From a DNA sample
24. Triassic
25. 64 million years ago

Twentieth Century World Leaders

1. Austrian
2. Harry S Truman
3. Chairman Mao
4. Fidel Castro
5. Harold Macmillan
6. Watergate Building, Washington DC
7. Golda Meir
8. General Charles de Gaulle
9. Roberts
10. Saddam Hussein
11. Saxophone
12. Mahatma
13. General Mussolini of Italy
14. 'I have a dream'
15. Nelson Mandela
16. Joseph Stalin
17. Governor of California
18. Winston Churchill
19. Colonel (Qaddafi)
20. Mrs. Bandaranaike
21. Rudolph Hess
22. Milhous
23. Mrs. Indira Gandhi
24. Mikhail Gorbachev
25. Harold Wilson

Pot Luck

1. The ear
2. Vitamin C
3. '... it would be necessary to invent him'
4. Tap
5. Pentateuch
6. Michelangelo
7. Zloty
8. Hydrogen and oxygen
9. Captain Ahab
10. Yellow
11. Q and Z
12. Mothballs
13. Wind velocity
14. Ants
15. Glenn Miller
16. Yom Kippur
17. Lewis Carroll
18. Scars
19. On the moon
20. Jolly Roger
21. Outer Hebrides
22. A munro
23. The kukri
24. Bluebird
25. Topiary

Quiz

1 Which city was said to have been founded by Romulus and Remus?

2 Name the race of warrior women, famed for their exploits in the Trojan war and ruled by a queen.

3 The Muses were the goddesses of poetry and song. How many Muses were there?

4 Poseidon was the Greek god of the sea. What did the Romans call him? ▲

5 Orpheus went down to Hades to rescue his wife. What was her name?

6 What is the usual occupation of the leprechaun of Irish legend?

7 Where did the Greek gods live?

8 Who led the Argonauts in search of the golden fleece?

9 Which Arabian princess saved her life by telling stories for 1001 nights?

10 What nationality was the legendary hero William Tell, who shot an apple from his son's head? ▶

11 Which Roman god gave his name to the month of January?

12 Which hero killed the Gorgon, Medusa?

13 How did the German maiden called Lorelei lure sailors on the River Rhine to their death?

14 The beauty of a woman, the daughter of Zeus, led to a war between Greece and Troy, so her face was said to have 'launched a thousand ships'. What was her name?

15 The Greek forces besieged Troy for 10 years before they devised a plan to smuggle soldiers into the city. How was this accomplished?

16 What was the name of the one-eyed giant of Greek mythology?

17 How was the sword of Damocles suspended?

18 What happens to those who kiss the Blarney Stone in Ireland?

19 Tales of King Arthur and the Knights of the Round Table have been popular since the Middle Ages. Which musical film, starring Richard Harris, told the story of Arthur and his court?

20 Who was the ancient Egyptian god of the sun?

21 Which character in Greek mythology died when he flew too close to the sun and melted his wings?

22 The Greeks called the goddess of the hunt Artemis. What was the Roman name for this goddess?

23 Which hero did Ariadne, the daughter of the great King Minos, help to escape from the Labyrinth?

24 In ancient Greek mythology, who was the famous winged male messenger who served all gods?

25 In the film *Robin and Marian* (1976) Audrey Hepburn played an elderly Maid Marian. Which male film star played opposite her as Robin Hood?

1 What was Tina Turner's original name? ▲ ▶

2 Who was the drummer who replaced the late Keith Moon in The Who in 1978?

3 Where is Gracelands, the mansion built for Elvis Presley, situated?

4 Which pop star's guitar sold for £198,000 at auction in 1990?

5 In which year did the Live Aid concerts take place?

6 What do the groups En Vogue, Jade and SWV have in common?

7 What is Bruce Springsteen's nickname?

8 Which pop artist recorded the album *True Blue* that topped the charts in 28 countries in 1986?

9 Which rock star became chairman of Watford Football Club in 1980?

10 What is 'acid house'?

11 Johnny Rotten and Sid Vicious belonged to which pop group?

12 Which world famous West Indian rock star, a friend of Jamaican Prime Minister Michael Manley, was shot in the arm by political opponents in 1976?

13 Whose album entitled *Tattoo You* was released in 1981?

14 Which city was the original home of the 1980s pop group U2?

15 Which legendary British singer was awarded the OBE by the Queen in 1980 on his 40th birthday?

16 On which of Michael Jackson's best-selling albums would you find the track *The Girl is Mine*?

17 Which band was the leader of the hard rock movement?

18 Which two artists founded the Eurythmics and recorded the first album in 1981?

19 In what film did pop star David Bowie launch his career as a film actor in 1976?

20 Their album *Synchronicity* became one of the best-selling LPs of all time and, in 1983, they reached No 1 in Britain and the United States with *Every Breath You Take*. Name the group.

21 Which of the Bee Gees are twins?

22 Who left an all-girl vocal group, originally called the Primettes, to begin a solo career in 1969 and has become a top international star?

23 Which American superstar said, 'I don't know anything about music. In my line you don't have to.'?

24 Who had a hit with *I Will Always Love You*?

25 Which American record label was bought by Polygram in August 1993?

1 What is the meaning of the Dutch word *brandewijn* from which we take our word brandy?

2 From which fruit is Calvados made?

3 Which drink has been known as 'Dutch courage' and 'Mother's ruin'?

4 Between 1740 and 1970 British sailors received a daily ration of grog. What is grog? ▼▶

5 5. What is the name of the Japanese spirit made from rice which is served warm?

6 Schnapps is made in Germany from potatoes. What is used for flavouring?

7 Where did the American whiskey 'Bourbon' get its name?

8 What is added to gin to make pink gin?

9 Bottles of spirits should be stored upright. Why? ▶

SIX-WATER GROG.

10 Advocaat is a low-alcohol liqueur made from brandy, sugar and what other important ingredient?

11 Cognac can be made only in a specific area of France. Where can brandy be made?

12 The fermented molasses left over from the sugar-refining process is used in the manufacture of which spirit?

13 A popular Yorkshire liqueur flavoured with herbs is named after the Brontë sisters. On which spirit is it based?

14 In which country is Geneva gin made?

15 What colourless liqueur is made from cherries?

16 Poteen is an illegally distilled spirit made in the west of Ireland. What is it made from?

17 What colour is the Italian liqueur Galliano?

18 Atholl Brose is made from malt whisky, distilled oatmeal, honey and what else?

19 What do the letters VSOP on a bottle of brandy stand for?

20 Southern Comfort is a popular American liqueur with a base of Bourbon whiskey and a fruit flavouring. Which fruit?

21 What is the flavouring of Pernod, the French spirit that turns milky when water is added?

22 Which liqueur is made from the peel of small bitter oranges?

23 What type of spirit is Bacardi?

24 A well-known Balkan spirit is made from plums. What is it called?

25 How old must Scotch whisky be before it can be sold in the U.K.?

1 Where were the 1992 Olympics held?

2 Do Olympic rules allow competitors in athletics events to go without shoes?

3 What distance is the Olympic marathon?

4 How long is the run-up for the Olympic high jump?

5 The modern pentathlon includes fencing, cross-country running, riding, shooting and one other event. What is it?

6 The women's pentathlon has been dominated by East German athletes, but in 1972 there was a British winner. Name her.

7 Which Romanian gymnast won six individual gold medals in 1976-80, sometimes achieving perfect scores?

8 Which country hosted the 1992 Winter Olympics?

9 How many consecutive failures are pole vaulters allowed before they are eliminated?

10 Two styles of wrestling are included in modern Olympics. One is Greco-Roman. What is the other?

11 Ben Johnson of Canada was disqualified in the 1988 Olympic Games in Seoul. Why? ▶

12 Throwing events in the Olympics include javelin, shotput and discus. What is the fourth? ▲

13 In javelin throwing, a red flag indicates a foul. What indicates a fair throw?

14 Which young gymnast from the U.S.S.R. won the hearts of the crowd for her original and individualistic style in the 1972 Munich Olympics?

15 In which decade was judo made an Olympic sport?

16 The three–day event includes three equestrian competitions. Two of them are show-jumping and endurance. What is the third?

17 What is the difference between the vaulting horse used in men's and women's gymnastics?

18 In ice dancing, how long is the free dance programme?

19 How many judges are involved in triple jump events?

20 Mark Spitz won seven gold medals at the 1972 Munich Olympics. In which sport did he compete?

21 What length is the swimming pool in which Olympic competitions are held?

22 What are the two middle distance Olympic track races?

23 How many events are included in the heptathlon?

24 The equestrian events of the Melbourne Olympics in 1956 were held in another country because of Australian quarantine regulations. Where were they held?

25 Who is the most recent British athlete to be simultaneously the World, Olympic, European and Commonwealth champion in his event?

1 What is the holy book of the Islamic religion called?

2 Followers of which religion use prayer wheels?

3 What is the name of the four-cornered headgear worn by Roman Catholic ecclesiastics? ▼

4 Which Christian saint was born at Lourdes in France?

5 What name is given to food prepared in accordance with Jewish ritual?

6 In which country are cows considered sacred?

7 Which religious movement was founded by Mary Baker Eddy in the 19th century?

8 Who was the only Englishman to become pope?

9 What is the tower on top of a Moslem mosque called? ▶

10 In the Islamic world, what is the Hajj?

11 In which country is Zen the leading school of Buddhism?

12 In the Christian religion, what name is given to the first day of Holy Week?

TOMB OF SULTAN KAITBAY

13 In the Jewish faith, what is the religious coming of age of a 13-year-old boy called?

14 In which country did the Dalai Lama rule?

15 Which day of the week is the Moslem Sabbath?

16 Who was the first Christian martyr?

17 Where does the world's largest Mormon Temple stand?

18 How many points does the Star of David have?

19 In which religion is Diwali, the Festival of Light, celebrated?

20 According to the book of Genesis, which common fruit were Adam and Eve forbidden to eat by God?

21 In what type of building would you find a minbar and a mihrab?

22 Who said, the famous words 'Religion is the opium of the people'?

23 How many gospels are there in the New Testament?

24 Vishnu, Shiva and Ganesh play an important part in which religion?

25 What special name was given to the particular-chalice used by Jesus Christ on the evening of the last supper?

1. What is the other name for the Northern Lights?

2. CFCs are said to be damaging the ozone layer. What does CFC stand for?

3. When you cross the international date line from east to west do you gain or lose a day?

4. What are the grasslands of North America called?

5. Which is the world's largest ocean?

6. What is the earth's outer layer called?

7. Why do farmers in parts of China keep ducks in their rice fields?

8. Corals grow in warm, tropical waters. What are corals made from? ▶

9. What is the longest river in Asia?

10. According to scientists, the Himalayas are about 40 million years old. Are the North American Rockies older or younger?

11. What are the chinook, the khamsin and the sirocco?

12. Which limestone formations hang down from the ceilings of caves: stalactites or stalagmites? ▶

13. What is a tsunami?

14. The earth is surrounded by a blanket of air. What is it called?

15. Bamboo forests grow in the south–western mountains of China, but bamboo is not a tree. What is it?

16 Some beaches, for instance in Tahiti, are made from lava. What colour is the sand?

17 In which lake in Peru do people live on islands built from thickly matted totora reeds?

18 What instrument is used for measuring atmospheric pressure?

19 In many countries, farmers cut down and burn a patch of forest, and then use the ash from the fire to fertilize crops. What is this method of cultivation called?

20 What protective function does the ozone layer fulfil?

21 21. What is the only grass that can actually grow in water?

22 22. How long does it take for the earth to revolve once on its axis?

23 23. What is the Hindu Kush?

24 24. What are cone-bearing trees called?

25 25. Half the entire desert area of the world is contained in just a single desert. Name it.

1 During Prohibition, Americans drank illegally in clubs. What were these places called?

2 Who spoke the first words in the first 'all singing, all dancing' film *The Jazz Singer*?

3 What were 'Oxford bags'?

4 By what nickname was French designer Gabrielle Chanel always known? ▲

5 Who followed the yellow brick road in *The Wizard of Oz* along with Dorothy and her dog?

6 What discovery set off the fashions in clothes, fabrics and footwear known as Tutmania?

7 What famous dance of the 1920s shared its name with a city in the southern United States? ▶

8 Which film cartoon character made his debut in *Steamboat Willie* in 1928?

9 Who was the British Prime Minister when King Edward VIII abdicated?

10 What was the other name for the men's fashion of knickerbockers?

11 The struggle for votes for women was finally successful in Britain in 1918. What was the voting age for women at the time?

12 The British called the fashion-conscious young people of the 1920s 'bright young things'. What were they called in America?

13 What film character was portrayed by American Olympic gold medallist swimmer Johnny Weissmuller?

14 In which sport was Frenchwoman Suzanne Lenglen famous, delighting crowds with her fashionable outfits?

15 Who was Ginger Rogers' famous dancing partner in musicals such as *Top Hat*?

16 What were Kickin' the Mule, Truckin' and Peckin' the Apple?

17 What type of skirt was a dirndl?

18 What famous skyscraper with 102 storeys was built in New York in 1931?

19 One of the most famous gangland killings in the United States took place on 14 February, 1929, when members of Al Capone's gang gunned down seven unarmed rivals. What was the killing known as?

20 Which President of the United States brought in the 'New Deal' to revive the American economy in the 1930s?

21 What new fabric replaced rayon for stockings in 1930?

22 German film maker Leni Riefenstahl was commissioned by Hitler to make a documentary of which event, aimed at glorifying Germans as the 'master race'?

23 Which British Prime Minister promised that the treaty signed with Germany in September 1938 meant 'peace in our time'?

24 Who starred as the glamorous nightclub singer in *The Blue Angel*?

25 What record did racing car driver Sir Malcolm Campbell break at Daytona Beach, Florida, in 1932?

1 What is the Decalogue usually called?

2 What is the name of Italy's state airline?

3 Which American golfer has been nicknamed the 'Golden Bear'?

4 Which London tube line is coloured green on the underground map?

5 The handsome peacock belongs to which family of birds? ▲

6 What does a Geiger counter measure?

7 In the fight for racial equality, black people in an American state organized a boycott of buses in 1955 to protest against race laws. Which state?

8 In 1960 Amy, Sally and Mo made a space flight. Who or what were Amy, Sally and Mo?

9 From which ancient game does badminton derive? ▶

10 In which country does the River Rhine rise?

11 In which novel does the parrot called Captain Flint appear?

12 Which young actor died in a car crash in California in 1955?

13 What would you expect to find in a sarcophagus?

14 In the Bible, who was Bathsheba's first husband, at the time when she caught King David's eye?

15 What does the term AWOL mean to a soldier?

16 In World War II, what was the Manhattan Project?

17 In what field was Maria Montessori famous?

18 The film *Ring of Bright Water* told the story of which type of creature?

19 Before British coinage was decimalized, how many old pennies made a florin?

20 In which sport did Mike Gatting become famous?

21 What was Beethoven's first name?

22 Count' was the nickname of which jazz musician?

23 What type of furniture is a davenport?

24 Name the official record of the daily proceedings in the British Parliament.

25 Which country is known as the 'land of the midnight sun'?

People and Places   Myths

1. Rome
2. Amazons
3. Nine
4. Neptune
5. Eurydice
6. Shoemaker
7. Olympus
8. Jason
9. Sharazad (Shéhérazade)
10. Swiss
11. Janus
12. Perseus
13. She sat on a rock combing her hair and singing
14. Helen
15. They hid inside a wooden horse
16. Cyclops
17. By a single hair
18. They acquire the 'gift of the gab'
19. Camelot
20. Ra
21. Icarus
22. Diana
23. Theseus
24. Hermes
25. Sean Connery

Entertaining Arts   Pop Music

1. Annie Mae Bullock
2. Kenny Jones
3. Memphis, Tennessee
4. Jimi Hendrix
5. 1985
6. All-girl groups
7. The Boss
8. Madonna
9. Elton John
10. A style of fast-beat pop music; also used for a youth cult associated with the music and sometimes with drug-taking
11. The Sex Pistols
12. Bob Marley
13. Rolling Stones
14. Dublin, Ireland
15. Cliff Richard
16. Thriller
17. Led Zeppelin
18. Annie Lennox and Dave Stewart
19. The Man who Fell to Earth
20. The Police
21. Maurice and Robin
22. Diana Ross
23. Elvis Presley
24. Whitney Houston
25. Motown

Food and Drink   The Hard Stuff

1. Burnt wine
2. Apples
3. Gin
4. A mixture of rum and water
5. Sake
6. Caraway seeds
7. It was first made in Bourbon County, Kentucky
8. Angostura bitters
9. To prevent the liquid coming in contact with the metal cap
10. Egg yolks
11. Anywhere in the world
12. Rum
13. Brandy
14. Holland
15. Kirsch
16. Potatoes
17. Yellow
18. Cream
19. Very Special Old Pale
20. Peach
21. Aniseed
22. Curaçao
23. White rum
24. Slivovitz
25. Three years

Sports and Pastimes   The Olympics

1. Barcelona, Spain
2. Yes
3. 42.195 km (26 miles 385 yards)
4. Unlimited
5. Swimming
6. Mary Peters
7. Nadia Comaneci
8. France
9. Three
10. Freestyle
11. Positive drugs test
12. Hammer
13. A white flag
14. Olga Korbut
15. 1960s
16. Dressage
17. The men's is higher; 135 cm compared with 120 cm
18. Four minutes
19. Five
20. Swimming
21. 50 metres
22. 800 metres and 1,500 metres
23. Seven
24. Stockholm, Sweden
25. Lindford Christie

History   World Religions

1. Koran
2. Buddhism
3. Biretta
4. Bernadette
5. Kosher
6. India
7. Christian Science
8. Nicholas Breakspear, Pope Hadrian IV
9. Minaret
10. Pilgrimage to Mecca
11. Japan
12. Palm Sunday
13. Bar Mitzvah
14. Tibet
15. Friday
16. St. Stephen
17. Salt Lake City
18. Six
19. Hindu
20. The fruit of the tree of knowledge of good and evil
21. A mosque
22. Karl Marx
23. Four
24. Hindu
25. The Holy Grail

Natural World   Our Earth

1. Aurora borealis
2. Chlorofluorocarbons
3. Lose a day
4. Prairie
5. Pacific
6. Crust
7. To control insect pests
8. Skeletons of millions of tiny creatures
9. The Yangtze
10. Older
11. Winds
12. Stalactites
13. A sea wave created by an earthquake
14. The atmosphere
15. A type of grass
16. Black
17. Lake Titicaca
18. Barometer
19. Slash and burn
20. It filters out the sun's harmful ultra-violet rays
21. Rice
22. 24 hours
23. A mountain range
24. Conifers
25. Sahara

Twentieth Century   The 1920s and 1930s

1. Speak-easies
2. Al Jolson
3. Wide-legged trousers
4. Coco
5. The cowardly lion, the scarecrow and the tin man
6. The tomb of Tutankhamen, the Egyptian boy king
7. The Charleston
8. Mickey Mouse
9. Stanley Baldwin
10. Plus-fours
11. 30
12. Flappers
13. Tarzan
14. Tennis
15. Fred Astaire
16. Dances
17. A full skirt, loosely gathered onto a waistband
18. Empire State Building
19. The St. Valentine's Day Massacre
20. President Roosevelt
21. Nylon
22. The Berlin Olympic Games in 1936
23. Neville Chamberlain
24. Marlene Dietrich
25. World land speed record

Pot Luck

1. The Ten Commandments
2. Al Italia
3. Jack Nicklaus
4. District
5. Pheasant
6. Radioactivity
7. Alabama
8. Mice
9. Battledore and shuttle cock
10. Switzerland
11. Treasure Island
12. James Dean
13. A corpse
14. Uriah the Hittite
15. Absent without leave
16. Development of the atomic bomb
17. Education
18. Otter
19. 24
20. Cricket
21. Ludwig
22. Basie
23. Writing desk
24. Hansard
25. Norway

Quiz

3

1. By what name is the Central Criminal Court in London better known?

2. Braemar, near Balmoral, is the site of the most famous of the great clan events, with competitions like caber tossing and hammer throwing. What are these events called?

3. What are Watling Street and Fosse Way?

4. Which Scottish loch is reputedly the home of a prehistoric monster?

5. On which river does the university town of Cambridge stand?

6. Which family trio of writers lived at the Parsonage in Haworth on the wild North Yorkshire moors?

7. Lewis, Harris and Benbecula are part of which group of Scottish islands?

8. Which London street is associated with the medical profession?

9. The Cistercian Abbey of Tintern, founded in 1131, stands beside the River Wye. Which 19th–century poet wrote *Lines written above Tintern Abbey*?

10. Which northern city is the home of the Royal Liver Building, two cathedrals and the Albert Dock?

11. What is the name of the Prime Minister's official country residence?

12. Which is the largest of the lakes in Cumbria's Lake District?

13. Chartwell, in Kent, was the home of which famous statesman for 40 years?

14. In which Midlands town is William Shakespeare buried at St. Mary's Church?

15 What is the nickname of the clock tower on the Houses of Parliament?

16 In which city would you find the Radcliffe Camera, the Sheldonian Theatre and Balliol College?

17 Which is the oldest British royal residence still in use?

18 Which river was the setting for the comic adventures of Jerome K. Jerome's *Three Men in a Boat* ?

19 In what part of the British Isles is the Brecon Beacons National Park?

20 What is the most southerly tip of England called?

21 One of Northern Ireland's most famous sights is a collection of basalt columns caused by the cooling and shrinking of lava from an ancient volcano. Legend says they were stepping stones used to reach Scotland. What are they called? ◀ ▲

22 The tors on Dartmoor in south-west Devon are the remains of a three million-year-old mountain system. From what type of rock are the tors formed?

23 In 122AD, a Roman emperor began the building of a wall across the north-west of England to mark the limits of the empire. What was his name?

24 Which Scottish glen is known as the 'Glen of Weeping' because it was the scene of a notorious massacre of the Macdonalds by the Campbells in 1692?

25 The Italianate village of Portmeirion in Wales was designed by Clough Williams-Ellis and provided an atmospheric setting for which 1960s hugely popular television series starring Patrick McGoohan?

1. Which character travelled around the world in 80 days with Passe Partout?

2. What was the girl's school created by Ronald Searle and portrayed in several comedy films?

3. Which author created the aggressive, lethal plants called triffids?

4. Name the Scottish schoolteacher played by Maggie Smith in the film of Muriel Spark's novel?

5. According to Aesop's Fable, which animal did the tortoise beat in a race?

6. Who wrote *The Last of the Mohicans*?

7. Name the young hero of *Treasure Island*.

8. In which book by William Golding are Piggy and Ralph shipwrecked?

9. Victor Hugo wrote *The Hunchback of Notre Dame*. What was his other famous book, the story of an escaped convict, Jean Valjean?

10. Which character in *David Copperfield*, by Charles Dickens, always insisted that he was 'very 'umble'?

11. In what London street did Sherlock Holmes live?

12. Under what name is the author Samuel Langhorne Clemens better known?

13. In which novel does the heroine finally marry Mr. Rochester?

14. Whom did Minnehaha marry in Longfellow's poem?

15. Peter Ustinov has portrayed Agatha Christie's detective Hercule Poirot in films. What nationality was Poirot?

16 In a 17th–century novel, Don Quixote decides to become a knight. What does he begin attacking because he mistakes them for a row of giants?

17 By what romantic name was Sir Percy Blakeney known in Baroness Orczy's novel?

18 Which novelist wrote of a farm run by pigs and of the imaginary world of 1984?

19 Name the character who visits Lilliput and Brobdingnag. ◀ ▼

20 *Carrie* and *The Shining* were both successful films. Who wrote the novels on which they were based?

21 Which character lived at Sunnybrook Farm?

22 Which best-selling novelist was the youngest member of the British House of Commons in 1969?

23 Two novels by Alan Sillitoe were filmed in the 1960s. One was *The Loneliness of the Long Distance Runner.* What was the other?

24 Jeeves was the perfect butler. Who was his employer?

25 In 1991 the sequel to *Gone with the Wind*, written by Alexandra Ripley, was published. What was the title?

1 What type of dried fruit do nomadic tribes call 'bread of the desert'?

2 What colour is the flesh of an ogen melon?

3 The plaintain is a staple food in some areas of East and West Africa. What type of fruit is it exactly?

4 'Plashing' is a term used to describe the collecting of which type of nut?

5 A number of cacti produce edible fruit, but which is the only cactus fruit to be eaten widely? ▲

6 The nursery rhyme says, 'I had a little nut-tree, nothing would it bear, but...'. What did it bear?

7 Which fruit took its name from a shortening of Damascene or 'plum from Damascus'?

8 The people of the Hunza valley in northern Pakistan were said to live to a ripe old age because their diet was based on which dried fruit?

9 What are Blenheim, Lord Derby and Peasgood?

10 Which nut is used to make marzipan?

11 In Edward Lear's poem, on what fruit did the Owl and the Pussycat dine?

12 A nectarine is a smooth-skinned variety of which fruit?

13 What type of fruit is morello?

14 What is the more usual name for a Chinese gooseberry?

15 Mangoes are rich in which vitamin?

16 When the mutiny on the *Bounty* took place, the ship was making for the West Indies with a cargo of fruit trees. Which type of fruit was it?

17 What is the pineapple's top-knot of stiff, spiky leaves called?

18 Bananas grow on stems and the bunches of bananas are called 'hands'. What are individual bananas called?

19 What is the other name for paw-paw?

20 From what type of tree does the delicious pecan nut come?

21 Which fruit got its name because the flowers are said to resemble the crown of thorns worn by Jesus Christ?

22 What fruit sauce is traditionally served with turkey?

23 Which fruit has six sections divided by whitish membranes, each containing many pips embedded in juicy flesh, and causes difficult-to-remove stains?

24 What are 'love apples'?

25 Which type of nut is sometimes called a groundnut or earthnut? ▼

1 Which horse won the Grand National three times?

2 Which famous American horse race is nick-named 'Run for the Roses' because the winner receives a garland of roses in the shape of a horseshoe?

3 What is a baby horse called?

4 When riding, what are 'aids'?

5 In a rodeo, bronco riding is a standard event. What is the only piece of tack worn by the horse?

6 What is a drag–hunt?

7 Which extremely successful racehorse, bred by the Aga Khan, disappeared and was never seen again?

8 Lucinda Green is a well-known British rider in horse trials and holds the record for the most wins at the Badminton Horse trials. What was her double-barrelled maiden name?

9 Three major races make up the legendary American Triple Crown. Two are the Preakness Stakes and the Kentucky Derby. What is the third race?

10 Which major horse race, inaugurated in 1861, is held in Australia on the first Tuesday in November?

11 What is the unit of measurement used for horses?

12 The horse Milton won the King George V Gold Cup in 1990 and the Volvo World Cup in 1990-91, among other competitions. Who was its British rider?

13 What are a horse's parents called?

14 How can a horse's age be determined?

15 On which British race course is Boxing Day's King George VI steeplechase held?

16 In polo, what is a chukka?

17 How many fences are there in the Grand National?

18 In show jumping, how many penalty points are awarded the rider falls off?

19 How did the Derby get its name? ◀ ▲

20 What, on the race-track, is an 'outsider'?

21 What type of horse is a 'stayer'?

22 How old is a filly?

23 Early races in America were sprints over short distances. Which famous breed was developed for the purpose?

24 In racing, what is a 'maiden'?

25 What happens in the rules of show jumping when two or more riders have tied for first place?

1. In which country were the earliest fragments of paper discovered?

2. Who invented the telephone?

3. In the 1764, an Englishman, James Hargreaves, invented a machine that revolutionized the weaving industry. What was it called?

4. In what decade of the 20th century did electric refrigerators appear, revolutionizing food storage?

5. What were the given names of the Wright brothers, who were the first to achieve power-controlled flight in a full-sized aeroplane? ▲ ▶

6. In 1895 Wilhelm Röntgen made a discovery which was described at the time as 'probably the greatest landmark in the whole history of diagnosis' and is still important in medicine today. What was it?

7. The first hearing aid was invented in 1901. What did people use before that?

8. Many labels still bear the name of the man who invented frozen food. Who was he?

9. In which country were the first bars of chocolate made?

10. What did Louis Braille invent in 1829?

11 Which brothers invented the hot-air balloon, which first carried human passengers in November 1783?

12 The wheel was first used in Mesopotamia over 5,000 years ago. In which modern country is Mesopotamia?

13 What means of transport did Christopher Cockerell invent in the 1950s?

14 What was the very first breakfast cereal, invented by H.D. Perky, who happened to be an American lawyer?

15 When the newly-invented vacuum flask was about to be launched on the market, a competition was held to find a name and 'Thermos' was chosen. What does thermos mean?

16 In which decade of the 20th century was the aerosol invented?

17 Which inventor developed the first radio when experimenting in his parents' attic near Bologna?

18 What did the French brothers Auguste and Louis Lumière demonstrate in the 1890s?

19 The first traffic lights were put up in London in 1868. Where were they situated?

20 In 1909, Leo Baekeland made a plastic from chemicals found in coal tar. What was it called?

21 In which century was movable type first used in Europe?

22 Which doctor discovered penicillin by accident?

23 In the 1920s when Thomas Wall of London manufactured the first wrapped blocks of ice cream and sold them from tricycles in the street. What was the slogan on the front of the tricycles?

24 Who invented the modern ballpoint pen?

25 Who was the German immigrant to the United States who began making trousers out of tough material called 'jean'

1 What is an eagle's nest called?

2 What kind of bird did Noah first release from the ark once the rain had stopped?

3 Which bird sometimes builds its nest on top of a chimney?

4 Baby birds have an 'egg tooth', a small knob on the tip of the beak. What is it used for?

5 Ducks feed in three ways, as grazers, dabblers and divers. To which category do mallards belong?

6 Which bird is the national emblem of the United States? ▼

7 How many toes do most birds have?

8 In ornithology, what is a clutch?

9 Which birds are bred for racing?

10 What is the other name for the long-necked anhinga?

17 In the old song, which bird sang in Berkeley Square?

18 What materials does a swallow use to build its nest?

19 The scientific name of which bird is Pica pica?

20 What is the Californian condor's current claim to fame?

21 Which birds are associated with the Tower of London?

22 Where do wading birds find their food?

23 Which type of swan has a black and yellow face?

24 What is the name for the place where birds sleep?

25 If a bird is diurnal, what are its habits?

11 What is unique about the beak of the wrybill, a New Zealand plover?

12 Which bird lays its eggs in another bird's nest? ▲▶

13 What colour is a female blackbird?

14 Which bird lays the largest egg?

15 Name the film in which Burt Lancaster played a bird-loving prisoner.

16 Which African bird is the tallest bird of prey?

1 What was the name of the American Allied Commanding Officer in the Gulf War?

2 What was the name given to the political movement that aimed to create a secure home in Palestine for the Jewish people and which emerged in the early 20th century?

3 What were the Communist guerrillas of the Vietnam war called?

4 The Arabic word 'jihad' literally means 'struggle'. What is the current popular meaning?

5 In 1976, PFLP and Baader-Meinhof terrorists hijacked an Air France plane and landed at a Ugandan airport. The hostages were freed in a successful raid by Israeli forces. Where was the airport?

6 What was the name of the missiles launched by Iraq against Israel in the Gulf War?

7 Members of Britain's SAS stormed the Iranian embassy in London where Arab terrorists were holding hostages in May 1980. What does SAS stand for? ▶

8 An exotic dancer, Margareta-Gertruida Zelle, was arrested and shot for espionage in World War I. By what name is she better known? ▶

9 In 1982 Argentina invaded the Falkland Islands, maintaining that it had a legal claim to sovereignty. What do Argentineans call the islands?

10 On what Jewish religious festival did the Arab-Israeli war of 1973 break out?

11 In the Vietnam war, what was the name of the jellied petrol that sticks to and sets fire to anything it touches?

12 What is the name of the rebel faction waging war in Angola?

13 What group is dedicated to achieving independence of the Basque region of northern Spain?

14 What South African word means 'separate development' or racial segregation?

15 What is semtex?

16 What do the initials IRA stand for?

17 Name the 'red priest' of Haiti, backed in his attempt to regain control of the island by the United States government.

18 Anwar Sadat was assassinated in 1981. In which country?

19 What is the Intifada?

20 Which island was awarded the George Cross for gallantry in World War II?

21 Who was assassinated in June 1914, precipitating the outbreak of World War I?

22 Which side did UN forces support in the Korean War?

23 In what year did Iraq invade Kuwait?

24 Hezbollah is an anti-Israeli and anti-western group of Shi'ite Muslims formed in Lebanon in the 1980s. What does the name mean?

1 What does a herpetologist study?

2 In the United States, how many nickels would you get for a dime?

3 What is a John Dory?

4 Which Scottish school did both the Duke of Edinburgh and his son Prince Charles attend? ▼

5 What does a dermatologist study?

6 Which is the least used letter in the English language?

7 Name the mythological character sentenced to fall in love with his own reflection as a punishment for his pride?

8 In 1908, Kenneth Graham, an English bank clerk, wrote a book which has become a children's classic. What was it called?

9 It is sometimes called a gnu. What is its other name?

10 When milk sours, what acid is formed?

11 Two countries have been the most frequent hosts of the Winter Olympics. One is the United States; what is the other?

16 In medicine. what is known as a 'magic bullet'?

17 What name is given to a baby whale? ▼

18 Which fictional aviator had friends called Ginger and Algy?

19 How do frogs catch flies?

20 Only one American state has a name beginning with 'L'. Name it.

21 For which film and television role is Leonard Nimoy best known?

22 What is measured by the truss?

23 In the book by James Hilton, what was the profession of 'Mr Chips'?

24 The national flag of the Netherlands bears which three colours?

25 On which island did the mutinous crew from the *Bounty* make their home?

12 Which James Bond film starred Honor Blackman? ▲

13 Who was the author of *Our Mutual Friend*?

14 At the time of the French Revolution, what were tumbrels?

15 Which American gangster was known as 'Scarface'?

People and Places British Isles

1. Old Bailey
2. Highland Gathering or Games
3. Roman roads
4. Loch Ness
5. River Cam
6. The Brontë sisters
7. Outer Hebrides
8. Harley Street
9. William Wordsworth
10. Liverpool
11. Chequers
12. Lake Windermere
13. Winston Churchill
14. Stratford-upon-Avon
15. Big Ben
16. Oxford
17. Windsor Castle
18. Thames
19. Wales
20. Lizard Point, Cornwall
21. Giant's Causeway
22. Granite
23. Hadrian
24. Glencoe
25. The Prisoner

Entertaining Arts A Good Read

1. Phileas Fogg
2. St. Trinian's
3. John Wyndham
4. Miss Jean Brodie
5. A hare
6. James Fenimore Cooper
7. Jim Hawkins
8. Lord of the Flies
9. Les Misérables
10. Uriah Heap
11. Baker Street
12. Mark Twain
13. Jane Eyre
14. Hiawatha
15. Belgian
16. Windmills
17. The Scarlet Pimpernel
18. George Orwell
19. Gulliver
20. Stephen King
21. Rebecca
22. Jeffrey Archer
23. Saturday Night and Sunday Morning
24. Bertie Wooster
25. Scarlett

Food and Drink Fruit and Nuts

1. Dates
2. Green
3. Cooking banana
4. Walnut
5. Prickly pear
6. A silver nutmeg and a golden pear
7. Damson
8. Apricots
9. Types of apple
10. Almond
11. Quince
12. Peach
13. Cherry
14. Kiwi fruit
15. Vitamin A
16. Breadfruit
17. Crown
18. Fingers
19. Papaya
20. Hickory tree
21. Passion fruit
22. Cranberry
23. Pomegranate
24. Tomatoes
25. Peanut

Sports and Pastimes Horses and Riding

1. Red Rum
2. Kentucky Derby
3. A foal
4. Any signals used by the rider to give instructions to the horse
5. A wide leather band round its middle, with a handhold
6. A hunt using an artificial scent
7. Shergar
8. Prior-Palmer
9. Belmont Stakes
10. Melbourne Cup
11. Hand
12. John Whitaker
13. Sire and dam
14. By examining its teeth
15. Kempton Park
16. The 4-6 periods into which the game is divided
17. 30, over two circuits
18. Eight
19. On the toss of a coin
between Lord Derby and Sir Charles Bunbury
20. A horse thought to have little chance of winning a race and therefore given long betting odds
21. A horse with great strength and endurance
22. Less than four years
23. The Quarter Horse
24. A horse of either sex which has not yet run a race
25. A jump-off

History Inventions

1. China
2. Alexander Graham Bell
3. Spinning jenny
4. 1920s
5. Wilbur and Orville
6. X rays
7. Ear trumpets
8. Clarence Birdseye
9. Switzerland
10. A system of raised dots to enable blind people to read printed words
11. Joseph and Etienne Montgolfier
12. Iraq
13. The hovercraft
14. Shredded Wheat
15. It is Greek for hot
16. 1940s
17. Gugliemo Marconi
18. Projected moving images
19. Outside the Houses of Parliament
20. Bakelite
21. 15th century
22. Dr. Alexander Fleming
23. 'Stop me and buy one'
24. Biró
25. Levi Strauss

Natural World Birds

1. An eyrie
2. Raven
3. Stork
4. To break out of the egg
5. Dabblers
6. Bald eagle
7. Four
8. The number of eggs a bird lays at one time
9. Homing pigeons
10. Snake-bird
11. It is the only bird with a beak that curves sideways
12. Cuckoo
13. Brown
14. Ostrich
15. Bird Man of Alcatraz
16. Secretary bird
17. Nightingale
18. Mud and saliva
19. Magpie
20. It is the rarest vulture in the world
21. Ravens
22. In the mud and sand at the water's edge
23. Bewick swan
24. Roost
25. It is active during the day and sleeps at nights

Twentieth Century Conflict and Conflagration

1. Norman Schwarzkopf
2. Zionism
3. Viet Cong
4. Holy war
5. Entebbe
6. Scud
7. Special Air Service
8. Mata Hari
9. Las Malvinas
10. Yom Kippur
11. Napalm
12. UNITA
13. ETA
14. Apartheid
15. Plastic explosive often used by terrorists
16. Irish Republican Army
17. Jean-Bertrand Aristide
18. Egypt
19. The Arab uprising in Israeli-occupied territory
20. Malta
21. Archduke Ferdinand of Austria
22. South Korea
23. 1990
24. Party of God

Pot Luck

1. Reptiles and amphibians
2. Two
3. A fish
4. Gordonstoun
5. Skin
6. Q
7. Narcissus
8. Wind in the Willows
9. Wildebeest
10. Lactic acid
11. France
12. Goldfinger
13. Charles Dickens
14. Horse-drawn wagons used to take prisoners to the guillotine
15. Al Capone
16. A drug that will attack only unhealthy ce ls
17. A calf
18. Biggles
19. They have sticky tongues
20. Louisiana
21. Mr. Spock
22. Hay or straw
23. Schoolteacher
24. Red, white and blue
25. Pitcairn

Quiz

4

1. How did the boy David defeat the giant Goliath?

2. What was the nickname of Ivan IV, Tsar of Russia in the 16th century?

3. Which American soldier, who led the Allied forces to victory in Europe in World War II, later became President of the United States?

4. How did Lawrence of Arabia die? ▼

5. Which Roman emperor was said to have fiddled while Rome burned?

6. Which people were led by Genghis Khan?

7. In 1939 Douglas Bader was flying Spitfire fighter planes for the RAF. Why was this extraordinary?

8. Which king of Judea ordered the massacre of male babies under the age of two?

9 How many terms did George Washington serve as the first President of the United States of America?

10 Many legends attach to the English highwayman Dick Turpin, hanged at Tyburn in 1739. According to legend, what was the name of his horse?

11 Who set off on Antarctic expeditions first in *Discovery* and later in *Terra Nova*?

12 Joseph Dzhugashvili, who succeeded Lenin as Soviet leader, took the name of Stalin. What does it mean?

13 The medical missionary Albert Schweizer was awarded the Nobel Peace Prize in 1952. What nationality was he?

14 How did the pirate Captain Kidd meet his end?

15 Which American President announced in 1863 that all slaves in the Confederate states would be freed immediately?

16 Whose secret police force was known as Ton-Ton-Macoutes?

17 Sir Thomas More was tried for high treason when he refused to recognize Henry VIII as Supreme Head of the Church. What high office did More hold?

18 An uprising of slaves against the Romans in 72BC was led by a Thracian gladiator, portrayed by Kirk Douglas in a 1960 film. What was his name? ▶

19 What is the meaning of *Mein Kampf*, the book which set out Hitler's political creed?

20 In which American city did the gangster Al Capone operate?

21 Davy Crockett made his name as a fearless pioneer and a soldier in the Indian wars before he was elected to Congress in 1827. Which state did he represent?

22 Which Hun leader united the Barbarian tribes and attacked the Byzantine Empire in 447?

23 Maximilien de Robespierre was one of the leaders of the French Revolution and ruled the country as a virtual dictator. What name was given to his period of rule?

24 Jean Bedel Bokassa had himself crowned Emperor Bokassa I of his country after it gained independence from the French. Which country was it?

25 Who dissolved the English Parliament and declared himself Lord Protector in 1653?

1. Which artist cut off the lobe of his ear and later shot himself?

2. What nationality were Brueghel and Rubens?

3. Which painter had a 'blue period'?

4. In which type of paintings did Sir Joshua Reynolds specialize?

5. Which legendary artist produced two versions of *The Madonna of the Rocks* between 1483 and 1508?

6. What is the largest oil painting in the world?

7. Where in Britain does Graham Sutherland's tapestry *Christ in His Majesty* hang?

8. Which famous painting by Leonardo da Vinci is also known as *La Gioconda*?

9. What was the great painter Michelangelo's other name?

10. The French Impressionist Edgar Degas is noted for his paintings of horse racing and what other subject?

11. Which actor played Henri Toulouse-Lautrec in the film *Moulin Rouge*?

12. *The Thinker* and *The Kiss* were among the works of which sculptor? ▶

13. Which English landscape artist painted *The Hay Wain* and *Flatford Mill*?

14. What style of painting, in which the subject is reduced to basic geometric shapes, was founded by Picasso and Braque?

15. Domenikos Theotocopoulos was a Greek-born painter who studied under Titian and then lived and worked in Spain. Under what name is he better known?

16. To which school of painting did Dante Gabriel Rossetti belong?

17. Sir Jacob Epstein established himself as a sculptor in Britain after studying in Paris. Where was he born?

18. To which school of painting did Claude Monet belong?

19. Canaletto was famous for his paintings of which city?

20. Who designed St. Paul's Cathedral in London?

21. Which artist was commissioned by the Italian city of Florence, to sculpt the figure of David?

22. What nationality was the painter Goya?

23. The French painter Paul Gauguin went to live and paint on a Pacific island. Which island was it?

24. For what subject was the painter Stubbs best known?

25. In which branch of the arts did Barbara Hepworth achieve fame?

1 What substance is added to some jams and marmalades to make them set so they are firm in consistency?

2 Fruit should never be cooked in a copper pan. Why not?

3 What is it called when fat and juices from the roasting tin are spooned over meat while it is cooking?

4 If you cook food at 220° Celsius, what Fahrenheit temperature would you use?

5 In Chinese cooking, what is the name of the curved–bottomed iron pan, in which food cooks very quickly? ▲

6 When cooking with eggs, what can be tested by putting the egg in water containing 10 per cent salt, to see if it sinks or floats?

7 Why would you decant red wine?

8 On which shelf of the refrigerator should raw meat be stored?

9 Blackcurrants are a good source of which vitamin?

10 In cooking, what is dredging?

11 What is the small ovenproof dish used to serve individual savoury portions of food called?

12 How many fluid ounces are there in an American pint?

13 How many fluid ounces are there in an Imperial pint?

14 What is parboiling?

15 In what food is collagen found?

16 In degrees Fahrenheit, the boiling point of water is 212°. What is it in degrees Celsius?

17 What is the food made when fresh milk is artificially curdled by bacteria?

18 When you pit a cherry, what do you do?

19 What does rechauffé mean?

20 Name the red colouring matter obtained from a small Mexican beetle used to give shades of red and pink to food?

21 What is the name of the bowl used to help grind food and spices, used with a pestle? ▼

22 How would you reduce a liquid?

23 What are small cubes of fried or toasted bread sprinkled on soup called?

24 In Indian cooking, what is the name given to butter after it has been heated and then left to set?

25 Which word describes the action of tying or skewering a turkey into a good shape before cooking?

1 How many playing cards are there in a standard pack?

2 How do players advance around the board in a game of Snakes and Ladders?

3 3. In bridge, what are the major suits?

4 4. What are the tiles used to play dominoes often called?

5 5. The game of chess is probably 14 centuries old. In which country did it originate? ▶

6 6. A backgammon board is marked out in saw-tooth 'points' in two colours. How many points?

7 What game was officially ruled by Hoyle's Laws from its publication in 1760 to 1864?

8 In draughts, how many draughtsmen does each player have?

9 In which card game would you 'meld'?

10 What is the letter Q worth in Scrabble?

11 How many games are there in a rubber of contract bridge?

12 For what are tarot cards used?

13 In which board game would you buy and sell property?

14 How is the score usually kept in cribbage?

15 In gin rummy, how many cards are dealt to each player at the beginning of the game?

16 In mah jong, what combination of tiles is called a kong?

17 In chess, what is a gambit?

18 In pontoon, what is the point value of the picture cards?

19 In which game do you have to deduce who committed a murder?

20 How many picture cards are there in a standard pack of playing cards?

21 In the famous French game of boules, what is a baguette actually used for when one is playing?

22 How many blank tiles are there in the game of Scrabble?

23 What is the other name given to a castle in chess?

24 If you win a rubber in bridge, what have you done?

25 In darts, what does a dart in the outer bull score? ◄

1. Name two of the brothers of lawman and gun-fighter Wyatt Earp.

2. The notorious Judge Roy Bean dispensed his form of justice from a Texas saloon that he named 'The Jersey Lily', after an actress he admired. Who was she?

3. Which two army officers led the expedition which was to open up the American West in 1804 and establish the Oregon Trail?

4. In 1953 Doris Day played the title role in a film about a tough woman of the early West who reckoned she could out-shoot and out-drink any man. What was her name? ▼

5. What would a cowboy do with 'chaps'– a word taken from the Mexican *chaparejos*?

6. What was the surname of the notorious outlaw brothers Frank and Jesse?

7. Gold was first found in California on land belonging to pioneer John Sutter in 1848. What were the thousands of prospectors who joined the Gold Rush called?

8. Kit Carson was one of the best known of the 'mountain men', who worked as fur trappers. As the settlers moved west, he made himself invaluable in another capacity. What work did he choose?

9. Where did General Custer make his ill-fated 'last stand'?

10. Name one of the two great heroes of the American west who died in the battle of the Alamo at San Antonio, Texas.

11. What was the profession of gunfighter and gambler 'Doc' Holliday?

12. The following advertisement appeared in the newspapers of 1860. 'Wanted: Young, skinny, wiry fellows not over 18. Must be expert riders willing to risk death daily. Orphans preferred.' What was on offer to the applicants? ▲

13 Joseph Smith founded the Church of Jesus Christ of Latter Day Saints (the Mormons), but who led the Mormon pioneers on the trek west to the Salt Lake basin?

14 When the Plains people folded their tepees and prepared to follow the buffalo herds to better hunting grounds, they loaded their belongings onto sledges mounted on runners. We still use the Indian word for such sledges today. What is it?

15 Sitting Bull (1834-90) was one of the most famous native Americans of his time. What was his tribe?

16 What was the name of the gang headed by Butch Cassidy and the Sundance Kid? ▼

17 By what name was Colonel William Cody better known?

18 What were the Shawnee, Chisholm and Goodnight-Loving?

19 In 1939, John Wayne starred in John Ford's classic western *Stagecoach*. What role did he play?

20 In 1881 Sheriff Pat Garratt killed a young outlaw in Fort Sumner, New Mexico, after hunting him for a year. Who was he?

21 According to tradition, Davy Crockett habitually wore a particular item of dress. What was it?

22 In 1873 a new invention by Joseph Glidden made fencing land for cattle ranching much easier. What was it?

23 Name the celebrated gunfight that took place in Tombstone, in Arizona in October 1881.

24 The building of the great Pacific railway was called 'the grandest enterprise under God'. What did the Native Americans call the train?

25 What was the usual nickname of the graveyard outside town where the victims of gunfights were buried?

1. How many known planets are there in our solar system?

2. What was the name of the first man in space?

3. In what state in America is Cape Canaveral, one of the world's most important launching sites for space travel? ▶

4. A 'supernova' occurs every few hundred years. What is it?

5. Who, in 1962, was the first American launched into orbit?

6. Why is it impossible to get an overall picture of Venus using telescopes?

7. What is the name of the spaceship in the *Star Trek* films?

8. Neil Armstrong was the first man to step onto the moon in 1969. Who was the second? ▶

9. How many men have walked on the moon?

10. Once a rocket has left the launch site at Cape Canaveral, Johnson Space Centre takes over. Where is it?

11. Who was the Polish born founder of modern astronomy?

12. How long does it take for the Moon to pass through a complete cycle from new Moon to new Moon?

13. Who was Britain's first cosmonaut?

14. What 'first' did Soviet cosmonaut Alexei Leonov achieve in 1965?

15 Which planet was named after the Roman messenger of the gods?

16 When does a meteoroid actually become a meteorite?

17 The Strategic Defence Initiative (SDI) was launched in 1983 by United States President Ronald Reagan. What was the project nicknamed?

18 Which is in fact the solar system's largest planet?

19 Which is the solar system's smallest planet?

20 Who was the first American woman in space?

21 In 1971, Mariner 9 sent back to earth the first close-up pictures of which planet?

22 What do we call the event when the moon passes across the face of the sun.

23 Name the world's first satellite, launched in 1957 by the U.S.S.R.

24 Who directed the film *Star Wars* in 1977?

25 For what is Edmund Halley the second British Astronomer Royal best known?

1. How often are Presidential elections held in the United States?

2. In which state was the first successful atomic bomb test held in July 1945?

3. What was the name given to the post-war rivalry between the Communist and non-Communist superpowers?

4. Which senator led the anti-Communist witchhunt of the early 1950s?

5. In the late 1960s demonstrators used to shout 'LBJ, LBJ, how many kids have you killed today?' About what were they protesting?

6. What were the first two names of Secretary of State Dulles, who served in Eisenhower's administration?

7. Who became President when Nixon was forced to resign in 1974?

8. What was the policy of transporting children from their own neighbourhood to school in other areas called?

9. Which singer made a comment on American society in *Times They Are A–Changin'* in 1965?

10. Under Jimmy Carter's presidency, the country suffered from 'stagflation'. What is 'stagflation'? ▲

11 What maximum speed limit was imposed on all roads after the oil shortages of the late 1970s?

12 The United States withdrew its athletes from the Moscow Olympics of 1980 as a protest against which action by U.S.S.R.?

13 Which President was nicknamed the 'great communicator'?

14 In which decade did Hawaii and Alaska become states of the Union?

15 By what name was the religious cult led by the Reverend Sun-Myung Moon popularly known?

16 Where in Washington does the United States Congress meet?

17 What do the initials CIA stand for?

18 Which city suffered an earthquake measuring 8.8 on the Richter scale in 1989? ▼

19 What did the press call the secret deal to sell arms to Iran in return for Iranian aid in freeing American hostages in the Lebanon?

20 Which United States Secretary of State engaged in 'shuttle diplomacy' in the conflict between Britain and Argentina over the Falkland Islands?

21 What street in New York is associated with financial dealings?

22 In the 1980s and 1990s drug abuse became a major issue. From what drug is the highly addictive 'crack' derived?

23 What is the name of New York's principal airport?

24 In the summer of 1980, a wave of race riots hit which American city?

25 The wreck of which famous ocean liner was found by an American and French team of divers in 1985?

1 In heraldry, what is the colour black called?

2 What famous Washington building would you find at 1600 Pennsylvania Avenue?

3 Which animal appears on the flag of Sri Lanka?

4 How many lines does a sonnet have?

5 Fronds are the leaves of what type of plant?

6 In which French city was Joan of Arc burned at the stake? ▼

7 To which country do the Atlantic islands, the Azores, belong?

8 The fantastically wealthy owner of a diamond mine gave his name to a southern African country that has since been renamed. Who was this man?

9 The Beatles founded their own record label. What was it called?

10 Name the virus that was deliberately introduced into Europe to control the rabbit population.

11 Where in the human body would one locate the cochlea?

12 What is the title of Beethoven's only opera?

13 What was the name of the lioness raised by Joy Adamson? ▲

14 One of Queen Elizabeth's four children was born at Clarence House. Which one?

15 The English call them nappies. What do the Americans call them?

16 What is non-rhyming poetry called?

17 In which country was Treblinka concentration camp?

18 Which district in Spain gave its name to sherry?

19 What is the common name for sodium hydroxide?

20 In architecture, what name is given to the horizontal beam over a door or window?

21 Name the type of cheese usually sprinkled on minestrone soup and spaghetti Bolognese?

22 What was Popeye the Sailor's favourite food?

23 At the wedding of Prince Charles, who acted as his best man?

24 What is pyrophobia?

25 Which organization has the motto 'Fidelity, Bravery, Integrity'?

People and Places   Heroes and Villains

1. He stunned him with a stone from a sling, then slew him with a sword
2. Ivan the Terrible
3. Dwight D. Eisenhower
4. In a motorcycle accident
5. Nero
6. Mongols
7. He had lost both legs
8. Herod
9. Two
10. Black Bess
11. Captain Scott
12. Man of Steel
13. French
14. He was hanged
15. Abraham Lincoln
16. 'Papa Doc' Duvalier
17. Lord Chancellor
18. Spartacus
19. My Struggle
20. Chicago
21. Tennessee
22. Attila
23. The Reign of Terror
24. Central African Republic
25. Oliver Cromwell

Entertaining Arts   Art and Artists

1. Vincent van Gogh
2. Flemish
3. Picasso
4. Portraits
5. Leonardo da Vinci
6. Paradise by Tintoretto
7. Coventry Cathedral
8. Mona Lisa
9. Buonarroti
10. Ballet dancers
11. Jose Ferrer
12. Rodin
13. John Constable
14. Cubism
15. El Greco
16. Pre-Raphaelite
17. United States
18. Impressionists
19. Venice
20. Sir Christopher Wren
21. Michelangelo
22. Spanish
23. Tahiti
24. Racehorses
25. Sculpture

Food and Drink   Kitchen Know-how

1. Pectin
2. Acid can dissolve the copper and cause poisoning
3. Basting
4. 425°
5. A wok
6. Freshness
7. To clear the sediment
8. Bottom shelf
9. Vitamin C
10. Sprinkling with sugar, flour, seasoning, etc.
11. Ramekin
12. 16
13. 20
14. Part cooking food which will then be cooked by another method
15. Meat and fish
16. 100°
17. Yogurt
18. Remove the stone
19. Reheating cooked food
20. Cochineal
21. Mortar
22. Boil it rapidly
23. Croûtons
24. Ghee
25. Trussing

Sports and Pastimes   A Quiet Game

1. 52
2. On rolls of a die
3. Spades and hearts
4. Bones
5. India
6. 24
7. Whist
8. 12
9. Canasta
10. 10 points
11. Three
12. Fortune-telling
13. Monopoly
14. On a pegboard
15. 10
16. A set of four identical tiles
17. Sacrifice of a piece or pawn at the opening
18. 10
19. Cluedo
20. 12
21. Measuring distance and tracing lines and marks
22. Two
23. Rook
24. Won two out of three games
25. 25

History   The Wild West

1. Morgan, Virgil, Jim, Baxter
2. Lillie Langtry
3. Lewis and Clark
4. Calamity Jane
5. Wear them
6. James
7. The Fortyniners
8. Scout
9. Little Bighorn
10. James Bowie and Davy Crockett
11. Dentist
12. A job as rider for the Pony Express
13. Brigham Young
14. Toboggan
15. Sioux
16. The Hole in the Wall gang
17. Buffalo Bill
18. Cattle trails
19. The Ringo Kid
20. Billy the Kid
21. Coonskin cap
22. Barbed wire
23. Gunfight at the OK Corral
24. The iron horse
25. Boot Hill

Natural World   Out in Space

1. Nine
2. Yuri Gagarin
3. Florida
4. The explosion of a star
5. John Glenn
6. The planet's surface is covered by thick cloud
7. Enterprise
8. Buzz Aldrin
9. 12
10. Houston, Texas
11. Copernicus
12. 29 days, 13 hours
13. Helen Sharman
14. First ever space walk
15. Mercury
16. When it strikes a planet
17. Star Wars
18. Jupiter
19. Pluto
20. Dr. Sally Ride
21. Mars
22. Solar eclipse
23. Sputnik I
24. George Lucas
25. His work on comets

Twentieth Century   The United States since 1946

1. Every four years
2. New Mexico
3. Cold War
4. Joseph McCarthy
5. Vietnam War
6. John Foster
7. Gerald Ford
8. Busing
9. Bob Dylan
10. A combination of stag2 nation and inflation
11. 55 mph
12. Invasion of Afghanistan
13. Ronald Reagan
14. 1950s
15. Moonies
16. Capitol Building
17. Central Intelligence Agency
18. San Francisco
19. Irangate
20. Alexander Haig
21. Wall Street
22. Cocaine
23. Kennedy airport
24. Miami
25. Titanic

Pot Luck

1. Sable
2. The White House
3. Lion
4. 14
5. Ferns
6. Rouen
7. Portugal
8. Cecil Rhodes
9. Apple
10. Myxomatosis
11. Inner ear
12. Fidelio
13. Elsa
14. Princess Anne
15. Diapers
16. Blank verse
17. Poland
18. Jerez
19. Caustic soda
20. Lintel
21. Parmesan
22. Spinach
23. No one. His two brothers were his 'supporters'
24. Fear of fire
25. FBI

Quiz

1 Cosa Nostra is another name for which secret society?

2 To which religion does a person with the surname Singh belong?

3 What has been the most frequent name for popes?

4 The first and last wives of Henry VIII had the same given name. Who were they?

5 In which sport did partners McNamara and McNamee compete?

6 What was the nickname of the landscape gardener Lancelot Brown?

7 In which film did Warren Beatty and Faye Dunaway play a pair of notorious outlaws?

8 Which United States President had the middle name Baines?

9 What was Judy Garland's real name? ◀

10 What was Iran called before 1935?

11 Name the three musketeers in the novel by Alexandre Dumas.

12 What was the artist Picasso's first name?

13 From which American President do teddy bears get their name?

14 What name did Peggy Hookham take for her career as a dancer?

15 What name is given to a community farm in Israel?

16 Which British politician was called 'the Welsh Wizard'?

17 The name of which Biblical character is given to someone thought to bring bad luck?

18 Which writer's given names were Pelham Grenville?

19 Who gave his name to the internationally known system of communication where letters appear as dots and dashes?

20 Which country has the name 'Hellas' on its postage stamps?

21 What was musician Louis Armstrong's nickname? ▼

22 Give the first name of German Field Marshall Goering.

23 What nickname is often given to people with the surname White?

24 In the Bond film Goldfinger what was the name of Goldfinger's bodyguard, who had a lethal hat?

25 What was the actual pen name of the world famous American writer William Sidney Porter?

1. What was the surname of Wendy and her brothers in Peter Pan?

2. In The Jungle Book, what type of animal is Baloo?

3. Who bullied Tom Brown at Rugby school?

4. The television series Little House on the Prairie was based on a series of books by Laura Ingalls Wilder. Who plays Laura in the series?

5. Who wrote about Christopher Robin and his friends, including Tigger and Piglet? ▲▶

6. In which pantomime does Widow Twankey appear?

7. Which is the first book to tell the story of Meg, Jo, Beth and Amy March?

8. What school did Billy Bunter, the 'fat owl of the Remove' attend?

9. In Enid Blyton's Famous Five stories, how many of the five are boys and how many are girls?

10. Which American author wrote Are you there, God?, It's me, Margaret and It's not the end of the World?

11. How many Dalmatians are there in the book and animated film titles?

12. Which book was written because C.L. Dodgson enjoyed telling stories to 10-year-old Alice Liddell and her sisters on an Oxford boat trip?

13. Who found a house made of bread and cake with window panes of sugar in a forest, and began eating bits of it?

14 What was the signature tune of the American cartoon character, Felix the cat?

15 In the Disney film Snow White and the Seven Dwarfs, the dwarfs were given names, including Happy, Sleepy, Doc, Bashful and Sneezy. Who were the other two?

16 Who lived at Green Gables?

17 How did Doctor Dolittle learn how to talk to animals?

18 Where was Superman born?

19 Which book, published in 1876, told the story of a boy who lives with his Aunt Polly in St. Petersburg, a village on the Mississippi?

20 In the film Bambi, what type of animal was Thumper?

21 Who created Skimbleshanks the cat?

22 In which film does Julie Andrews play a nursemaid with magic powers?

23 In the poem The Pied Piper of Hamelin by Robert Browning, the piper was engaged to rid the town of rats. When he was cheated of his payment, what did he do?

24 Which famous storyteller did Danny Kaye play in a film in 1952?

25 In the classic Uncle Tom's Cabin, who said 'Never had no father, nor mother, nor nothin'. I 'spect I growed'?

1 Which country is the world's largest producer of cheese? ▲

2 How many bottles of Champagne are there in a magnum?

3 From which country does 'Blood's Blood' come?

4 What type of milk goes into Roquefort cheese?

5 Commandaria St. John is the oldest known named wine and has been made since the 12th century. In which country is it made?

6 What do wine buffs call the scent given off by wine?

7 The bland cheese called Baby Bel was invented in 1931 in which country?

8 In which country are the wine-producing areas of Little Karoo, Ladysmith, Worcester and Montagu?

9 Which type of wine usually accompanies fish?

10 What word is used to describe a wine with a high alcohol content?

11 What do the Portuguese call the 'Englishman's wine'?

12 Which cheese, eaten all over the world, is transported in cylindrical wood-chip boxes?

13 What colour grapes are used to make white wine? ▼

14 The Rhenish wine, hock, takes its name from which German town?

15 What type of cheese is Dolcelatte?

16 How should bottles of wine be stored?

17 Which hard cheese is made from unpasteurized milk in certain provinces of the Po valley in Italy and matured from one to four years?

18 What does Appellation Origine Contrôllée on a bottle of French wine signify?

19 What is a non-vintage wine?

20 What is stored in a bodega?

21 Which European country is the world's largest wine producer?

22 What type of cheeses are native American products such as Colby, Monterey Jack and Tillamook?

23 The quality of Champagne, which is made only in a small area of France, is due to the great depth of what type of soil?

24 When sold in the United States, the Italian cheese Bel Paese has a map of the western hemisphere on the packet. What does the British packaging show?

25 Which English cheese, factory-made as early as 1870, is better known in its sage-flavoured, green-coloured version than in its original form?

1. How many times did Björn Borg win the men's singles finals at Wimbledon?

2. In which year did Monica Seles win her first U.S. Open?

3. Which championships make up the 'Grand Slam'?

4. What was Australian player Evonne Cawley's maiden name?

5. At what score does a tie-break come into operation?

6. What is the first score in a tennis match?

7. Jennifer Capriatti was Olympic singles champion in 1992. Which country does she represent?

8. What is the name given to a short, quick stroke when the ball is hit before it bounces?

9 Who was the only Afro-American man to win major tennis championships?

10 If part of the ball touches the baseline, is it in or out?

11 Name the film actress who married John McEnroe.

12 Which woman has won most Wimbledon singles titles?

13 In doubles matches the Australian formation is when both members of the serving team stand on the same side of their half of the court. What is the other name used for this formation?

14 Who was known as 'Little Mo'?

15 Name the woman tennis player who was undefeated on clay courts for 125 matches from August 1973 to May 1979?

16 In which country did the game of tennis originate in the Middle Ages?

17 Who was the youngest and the first unseeded player to win the men's singles at Wimbledon?

18 What is the name given to the centre of the racket strings, the best place to hit the ball?

19 Who was nicknamed 'Horrible Hana' by the British press?

20 American teams have recorded most wins in the Davis Cup tennis competion. Which country comes second?

21 Rod Laver is considered one of the best ever players. What was his home country?

22 How many Wimbledon singles titles did John McEnroe win? ◀ ▶

23 In the 1984 final of the French Open, John McEnroe took the first two sets and it looked as though the United States might win the title for the first time in 29 years. However, his opponent beat him to win his first major title. Who was he?

24 What is an 'ace'?

25 In practice, 'shadow stroking' is often used as a way of improving technique. What is it?

1 Where in the world was the Thirty Years War fought?

2 In which country did the Boxer Rebellion take place?

3 In the Second Punic War, a Carthaginian general led a whole army, including elephants, across the Alps and defeated the Romans at Cannae. What was his name?

4 The houses of York and Lancaster fought the War of the Roses. Which side had the white rose as its symbol?

5 In which war did Florence Nightingale lead a team of nurses? ▲

6 Kaiser Wilhelm I was ruler of Germany when World War I broke out. What did the British nickname him?

7 The Boston Tea Party contributed to the start of a war. Which war?

8 Which English king was killed at the Battle of Hastings in 1066?

9 Who fought the 100 Years War?

10 What contribution did Copenhagen make to the Battle of Waterloo?

11 The battle of Spion Kop was fought in Natal in 1900 in which war?

12 At the battle of Passchendaele in 1917, the British forces suffered 265,000 dead and wounded and gained only a few kilometres of mud. Where is Passchendaele? ▼

13 What type of weapon was the tomahawk, used by native North Americans?

14 In what year did the Russian Revolution take place?

15 Which war was named after an incident when an English sea captain lost an ear in a skirmish with the Spanish?

16 What were the two sides in the English Civil War called?

17 Which war was the longest in history?

18 What battle between the French and the English took place on St. Crispin's Day in 1415?

19 The film A Bridge too Far is about which battle?

20 After it had lost the War of American Independence, which part of North America did Britain retain?

21 Which famous English admiral died at the Battle of Trafalgar, living just long enough to hear that the battle was a great victory?

22 Who sent the Armada to conquer England?

23 Which famous battle in the American Civil War was the beginning of the end for General Robert E. Lee and the Confederate forces?

24 What colour was the Confederate uniform in the American Civil War?

25 Who invaded England in 55BC?

1 What organs enable fish to breathe under water?

2 What happens to a starfish if it loses an arm?

3 Which is the fastest sea mammal?

4 What are the tiny plants and animals that float in the top layer of the sea called?

5 Which birds breed on the soda lakes of East Africa?

6 What is an otter's home called?

7 How many tentacles has an octopus?

8 Dolphins often travel in family groups. What are they called? ▼

9 Why do spoonbills and flamingos swing their heads from side to side in water or mud?

10 Many fish have a swim bladder, like a bag of air, inside their bodies. What is its purpose?

11 Which river-living mammal has a duck-like beak and lays eggs?

12 The giant Victoria water lily of South America is the largest water plant. Which is the smallest?

13 What is the other name for a manatee?

14 What group of fish do lampreys and hagfish belong to?

15 What are limpets?

16 What does the huge (up to 12 metres long) whale shark eat?

17 What is a male swan called?

18 How do whales breathe?

19 What is unusual about the way the sea horse hatches its young? ▲

20 Where do demersal fish live?

21 What actually is the world's smallest living species of fish?

22 Which type of shark is the most dangerous to people?

23 Very rarely an occasional oyster miraculously produces a pearl. What causes this to happen?

24 Small fish almost always swim in groups for protection from predators. What are these groups called?

25 What is the correct terminology for an infant eel?

1. Which pop singer faced allegations of child sex abuse in California in 1993?

2. The Ayatollah Khomeini issued a death threat against novelist Salman Rushdie after the publication of which novel?

3. Why did Britain's Trade Secretary Cecil Parkinson resign during the Tory party conference in 1983?

4. In 1981 lorry driver Peter Sutcliffe pleaded guilty to 13 killings in the north of England. By what name is Sutcliffe popularly known?

5. Two reporters, Carl Bernstein and Bob Woodward, uncovered the Watergate scandal. Which newspaper employed them? ▲

6. Where was the Archbishop of Canterbury's special envoy Terry Waite kidnapped in 1987?

7. British MP John Stonehouse was arrested in Australia in 1974 on charges of theft and forgery. How had he attempted to cover his disappearance?

8. What controversial book did former intelligence officer Peter Wright publish in 1987?

9. Which foreign office Soviet spy defected to Moscow in 1951?

10. On which day of the week was John Lennon shot in New York?

11. Who was Joyce McKinney accused of kidnapping and forcing to make love to her in 1977?

12. What was the nickname given to Jack Kevorkian, the retired American pathologist who helped several people to commit suicide in the 1990s?

13 In October 1990 Marion Barry, Mayor of Washington DC, was given a six–month prison sentence and a $5,000 fine. What was his offence?

14 Intimate taped conversations allegedly between the Prince of Wales and an old friend caused a furore when they were published in the British press. What is the friend's name?

15 Which British politician won a libel action against a magazine that linked his name with that of caterer Clare Latimer in 1993?

16 16. In 1969 Senator Edward Kennedy's car plunged over a bridge at Chappaquiddick and a girl was killed. What was her name?

17 Which eminent judge conducted the British 'arms for Iraq' enquiry in 1993?

18 From what position was John Profumo forced to resign in 1963 after revelations about his affair with Christine Keeler?

19 Which American TV evangelist was sentenced to 45 years in prison in 1989 on 24 counts of fraud and conspiracy?

20 Which bank, in 1988, was charged with laundering money for cocaine traffickers?

21 Of what was Judge Clarence Thomas accused when he stood for appointment to the United States Supreme Court in 1991? ▼

22 Who was the 'Queen of Mean', wife of an American property tycoon, quoted as saying, 'only little people pay taxes', and eventually sent to prison for tax evasion?

23 Woody Allen's divorce made headline news when he was accused of child abuse. Who was his wife?

24 Which American rock singer died of a drugs' overdose at the age of 27 in October 1970?

25 In Britain, the Director of Public Prosecutions, Sir Allan Green, resigned his post after a caution from the police. What was his alleged offence?

1 In Alice's Adventures in Wonderland, whom did Alice join at a tea party, along with the Mad Hatter?

2 Which of the Seven Wonders of the Ancient World stood at Olympus?

3 The film Silkwood was based on a true case about nuclear industry safety hazards. Who played Karen Silkwood?

4 Which is the largest joint in the body?

5 According to the nursery rhyme, who is made from 'sugar and spice and all things nice'?

6 The backbone is a flexible chain of how many bones?

7 What is the fundamental oath usually associated with doctors?

8 Which designer created the fashion called the 'New Look'? ▼

9 Which extremist terrorist group coldly killed 11 world-class Israeli athletes at the Munich Olympics of 1972?

10 Which carnivorous animal lives wild in the Australian outback?

11 Who was 'The Equalizer' in the popular television series?

12 Into which ocean does the Zambesi river flow?

13 Where would you normally find a gavel?

14 Who wrote The Unfinished Symphony?

15 The centaur is a mythological creature, part man and part what?

16 Which school did Princess Anne attend?

17 What was Ringo Starr's original name? ▲

18 Who said 'If you can count your money, you're not really a rich man'?

19 To which group of mammals do apes and monkeys belong?

20 Which was the very first birth the Bible ever records?

21 What are the punched holes at the side of postage stamps called?

22 If you saw 'AP' on a print, what exactly would it mean?

23 What was Louise Brown's unique claim to fame-this century?

24 They may be complex, vulgar or mixed. What are they?

25 In the Book of Genesis, how many days did the Creation take?

People and Places Names and Such

1. Mafia
2. Sikh
3. John
4. Catherine of Aragon and Catherine Parr
5. Tennis
6. Capability
7. Bonnie and Clyde
8. Lyndon Johnson
9. Frances Ethel Gumm
10. Persia
11. Athos, Porthos and
Aramis
12. Pablo
13. Theodore Roosevelt
14. Margot Fonteyn
15. Kibbutz
16. David Lloyd George
17. Jonah
18. P.G. Wodehouse
19. Samuel Morse
20. Greece
21. Satchmo
22. Hermann
23. Chalky
24. Oddjob
25. O. Henry

Entertaining Arts Children's Corner

1. Darling
2. Brown bear
3. Flashman
4. Melissa Gilbert
5. A.A. Milne
6. Aladdin
7. Little Women
8. Greyfriars
9. Two of each
10. Judy Blume
11. 101
12. Alice's Adventures in
Wonderland
13. Hansel and Gretel
14. Felix Kept on Walking
15. Grumpy and Dopey
16. Anne
17. His parrot, Polynesia, taught him
18. The planet Krypton
19. The Adventures of Tom Sawyer
20. Rabbit
21. T.S. Eliot
22. Mary Poppins
23. He took the children of the town
24. Hans Christian Andersen
25. Topsy

Food and Drink Cheese and Wine

1. United States
2. Two
3. Hungary
4. Ewe's milk
5. Cyprus
6. Bouquet
7. France
8. South Africa
9. Dry white wine
10. Robust
11. Port
12. Camembert
13. Any colour
14. Hochheim, on the River Main
15. Soft blue cow's milk cheese
16. On their sides, preferably in the dark
17. Parmesan
18. It is a guarantee that quality wine comes from a defined area
19. A blend of wine from
different years
20. Sherry
21. Italy
22. Cheddar
23. Chalk
24. Map of Italy
25. Derby

Sports and Pastimes Tennis

1. Five
2. 1991
3. Wimbledon, U.S. Open, French Championship and Australian Championship
4. Goolagong
5. When the score reaches six games all
6. 15-love or love-15
7. United States
8. Volley
9. Arthur Ashe
10. In
11. Tatum O'Neal
12. Martina Navratilova
13. Tandem
14. Champion player Maureen Connolly
15. Chris Evert
16. France
17. Boris Becker
18. Sweet spot
19. Hana Mandlikova
20. Australia
21. Australia
22. Three
23. Ivan Lendl
24. A service too fast and accurate for the opponent to hit
25. Practising the motions of groundstrokes without hitting the ball

History Wars and Battles

1. Germany
2. China
3. Hannibal
4. York
5. Crimean War
6. Kaiser Bill
7. War of American Independence
8. Harold
9. France and England
10. Copenhagen was a horse; he carried the
Duke of Wellington
11. Boer War
12. Flanders
13. Short-handled axe or hatchet
14. 1917
15. The war of Jenkins' Ear
16. Cavaliers or Royalists and Roundheads or Parliamentarians
17. The Hundred Years War 1338-1453
18. Battle of Agincourt
19. Arnhem
20. Canada
21. Nelson
22. Philip II of Spain
23. Gettysburg
24. Grey
25. The Romans under Julius Caesar

Natural World At Home in the Water

1. Gills
2. It grows a new one
3. Killer whale
4. Plankton
5. Flamingos
6. Holt
7. Eight
8. Pods
9. They are filtering out food
10. It makes them lighter and helps them to float
in the water
11. The platypus
12. Algae
13. Sea cow
14. Agnatha or jawless
15. Sea snails
16. Plankton
17. A cob
18. Through blowholes on the top of the head
19. The male keeps the eggs in his pouch until
they hatch
20. At the bottom of the sea
21. A type of goby
22. The great white shark
23. A sand grain inside the shell
24. Shoals
25. Elver

Twentieth Century Alarm and Scandal

1. Michael Jackson
2. Satanic Verses
3. His affair with Sara Keays had become public
4. The Yorkshire Ripper
5. Washington Post
6. Beirut
7. He faked suicide
8. Spycatcher
9. Guy Burgess
10. Monday
11. Mormon missionary Kirk Anderson
12. Dr. Death
13. Possession of cocaine
14. Camilla Parker-Bowles
15. John Major
16. Mary Jo Kopechne
17. Lord Justice Scott
18. British Secretary of State for War
19. Jim Bakker
20. Bank of Credit and
Commerce International
21. Sexual harassment
22. Leona Helmsley
23. Mia Farrow
24. Janis Joplin
25. Kerb-crawling

Pot Luck

1. The March Hare and the Dormouse
2. Statue of Jupiter
3. Meryl Streep
4. Knee joint
5. Little girls
6. 26
7. Hippocratic oath
8. Christian Dior
9. Black September
10. Dingo
11. Edward Woodward
12. Indian ocean
13. An auction room
14. Schubert
15. Horse
16. Benenden
17. Richard Starkey
18. Paul Getty
19. Primates
20. Cain
21. Perforations
22. Artist's proof
23. The world's first test-
tube baby
24. Fractions
25. Six

Quiz

5 Which singer was known as the Swedish Nightingale?

6 What did Harriet Beecher Stowe do to help the lot of black slaves in America?

7 With what slogan are Emmeline Pankhurst and her daughters associated?

8 In which country was Israeli leader Golda Meir born?

9 Who was nicknamed 'the iron lady'?

10 The Nobel Peace prize was awarded to two Irish women in 1976. Maired Corrigan was one; who was the other?

11 What was Nancy Reagan's occupation before she devoted herself to helping her husband's political career? ◀

12 Which dancer, a soloist with Diaghilev's Ballet Russe, formed a London company which became, in 1957, the Royal Ballet?

13 Which 19th-century Englishwoman campaigned for prison reform?

14 Which of the Brontë sisters wrote The Tenant of Wildfell Hall?

15 Which famous opera singer left her husband for Greek shipping magnate Aristotle Onassis, who in turn left her to marry Jacqueline Kennedy?

16 In which film did Elizabeth Taylor achieve child stardom in 1944?

17 Joan Armatrading has achieved worldwide success as a vocalist and guitarist. Where was she born?

1 What nationality was Catherine the Great?

2 Which novelist wrote Emma and Mansfield Park?

3 Andrée de Jongh, known as Dédée, was 24 years old when she set up the Comet Line and was later awarded the George Medal by King George VI. What was the Comet Line?

4 In what field did Sarah Siddons achieve fame in the 18th century?

18 In the last nine years of her life, Sarah Bernhardt suffered from a physical disability, although she continued to act. What was the disability?

19 Who was the legendary 19th-century pioneer of women's rights in the British medical profession in which she qualified and was eventually finally allowed to practise as a doctor and after whom a very famous women's hospital in London was named?

20 Which young woman stabbed Jean Paul Marat, one of the leaders of the French Revolution, in his bath?

21 Gladys Aylward became famous for her missionary work in China. Who portrayed her in the film Inn of the Sixth Happiness?

22 Which American state is named for Queen Elizabeth I?

23 Who was the only person to win Nobel Prizes for Physics and Chemistry?

24 What is Mother Teresa's given name? ▼

25 Name the woman who was elected President of the Philippines after Ferdinand Marcos fled?

1 Which musical was derived from George Bernard Shaw's play Pygmalion?

2 Which New York composer wrote the score for A Chorus Line?

3 In the film Oklahoma, who played the villain Jud Fry?

4 An 'American Tribal Love-Rock Musical' first shocked and delighted audiences in the 1960s. What was it called? ▲

5 Which musical includes the songs Marrying for Love and Hostess with the Mostes' on the Ball?

6 On Broadway, Glynis Johns sang Send in the Clowns in A Little Night Music. On the London stage it was sung by Jean Simmons. Who sang it on screen?

7 In South Pacific, heroine Nellie Forbush falls in love with a plantation owner. What was Nellie's profession?

8 The Sound of Music, starring Julie Andrews on screen, told the story of which real-life family? ▶

9 In the film Oliver, Mark Lester played the title role. Who played the Artful Dodger?

10 Which musical, inspired by a comic strip, tells the story of an orphan who is eventually adopted by a millionaire?

11 Richard Rodgers and Oscar Hammerstein II formed the most successful of musical partnerships. Which was the lyricist?

12 Which author wrote the book on which the musical Les Misérables was based?

13 Who starred with Dorothy Dandridge in the 1959 film Porgy and Bess?

14 Which film musical, starring Liza Minelli, is set in Berlin during the rise of the Nazis?

15 The characters Gus, Skimbleshanks and Growltiger appear in which musical?

16 The film High Society, starring Grace Kelly, was a musical remake of which film?

17 The King and I told the story of a real-life English governess who went to teach the children of the King of Siam in Victorian times. What was her name?

18 Which musical told the story of a Scottish town that appears only once every 100 years?

19 Name the composer and lyricist who produced Gigi, Coco and Paint Your Wagon.

20 The songs June is Bustin' Out All Over and You'll Never Walk Alone come from which musical?

21 Who went 'Singin' in the rain' in the film of the same name?

22 Evita was based on the life of the wife of a South American dictator. Who was she?

23 Who starred as the young Gypsy Rose Lee in the film Gypsy?

24 Richard Harris starred in the film Camelot. Who sang his songs?

25 The actress Tammie Grimes played the title role in The Unsinkable Mollie Brown on Broadway. Who actually played Mollie Brown in the film?

1 What type of soup is a julienne?

2 The Italians and Americans call them zucchini. What do the French and British call them?

3 At what stage of the meal would you eat a charlotte?

4 Which region of France is the original home of Calvados?

5 What type of delicious food are the French langues de chat?

6 What name is given to a pan of hot water which stands on top of the cooker and in which other pans stand, so that their contents will cook gently?

7 What is Coquille St. Jacques a fancy name for?

8 What is the head waiter in a French restaurant called?

9 How is a drink served when it is described as frappé?

10 What name is given to a ham and cheese sandwich dipped in beaten egg and deep-fried?

11 When food is cooked en croûte, what does it mean?

12 What is the difference between pommes and pommes de terre?

13 What have you ordered if a thin pancake is cooked in butter, sugar, orange juice and Curaçao, and then flambéed at your table? ▲

14 Petit fours means literally 'little ovens', but what are they?

15 What is the main ingredient of a soufflé?

16 In a French restaurant, what describes a dish that is specially recommended that day?

17 Bénédictine has been made by the Bénédictine order since the 16th century. On what is it based? ▼

18 At what stage of the meal would you eat cassoulet?

19 What is a sorbet?

20 How is boeuf bourguignon cooked?

21 What type of stew is a navarin?

22 What is the most famous guide to the best restaurants in France called?

23 What is a clafouti?

24 If you ordered carré d'agneau, what would be served?

25 François-René de Chateaubriand was a novelist, poet and politician. What type of food was named after him?

1 What sport has a 'beach start' and a 'dock start'?

2 In boxing, which is lighter: bantamweight or featherweight?

3 In which sport are competitors forbidden to play left-handed?

4 Two methods are used in weight-lifting. One is the clean and jerk. What is the other?

5 When a referee in karate calls shobu sanbon hajime, what happens?

6 In curling, what is a broom used for?

7 How many rounds are there in a professional boxing title contest?

8 In which sport does one player take black and blue balls and another red and yellow?

9 In Rugby, which players form the scrum? ▼

10 How many games make up a match in squash?

11 Which piece of sporting equipment shares its name with a character from A Midsummer Night's Dream?

12 In table tennis, what is the name given to a rally where no points are scored? ▶

13 What is the value of the black ball in snooker?

14 On which hand does a right-handed hammer competitor wear a glove?

15 Which three events are included in the Olympic triathlon?

16 In the sport of sled-dog racing, what exactly is a musher?

17 In athletics, how many obstacles would you find in the 3,000 metres steeplechase?

18 Rifle shooting is divided into three basic categories. Two of them are smallbore and bigbore. What is the third?

19 What is the minimum height by which the bar of the Olympic pole vault is raised for each round?

20 How many players make up each team in volleyball?

21 Which is the first stroke in a medley relay in swimming?

22 A player called a 'goal attack' is found in which game?

23 How old must a horse be before it can take part in steeplechasing?

24 What do orienteering competitors often carry for use in an emergency?

25 Which sport includes coxless pairs and quadruple sculls?

1. Who invaded England during the reign of Alfred the Great, King of Wessex?

2. At the centre of a medieval castle, surrounded by walls and moats, was a tall tower. What was it called? ▲

3. Charlemagne was crowned Emperor in Rome in 800. What did his name mean?

4. Oxford and Cambridge universities were both founded in the Middle Ages. Which came first?

5. The Vikings were pirates who raided European lands in the 8th and 9th centuries. Where did they come from?

6. Thursday takes its name from one of the gods worshipped by the Vikings. What was the name of the god?

7. Which famous tapestry tells the story of the Battle of Hastings?

8. What was the name given to the mock fights between two mounted knights at tournaments? ▶

9. What building became a place of pilgrimage after Thomas a Becket was murdered there in the 12th century?

10. In 1096 Pope Urban II called for a crusade or 'war of the cross'. Where were the crusades fought?

11. Which country was ruled by the Shoguns from 1192?

12. Which young woman was known as the Maid of Orleans?

13. The Renaissance began in Italy around 1300. What does Renaissance mean?

14. In the Middle Ages, every monastery had its Physick garden. What grew there?

15 What was kept in a reliquary?

16 Every medieval castle would have its own bakery, granary and buttery. What was the buttery?

17 Who was the red-headed king who succeeded William I?

18 In the Middle Ages, what was a 'hospice' or hospital?

19 Which city did the Medicis rule?

20 In Norman England, knights leased small pieces of land to men who had to give free labour and obedience in return. What were these men called?

21 William the Conqueror ordered a detailed register of the lands of England. What was the resulting survey called?

22 What 14th century event does the nursery rhyme 'Ring a ring of roses' commemorate?

23 Which Englishman led the Peasants' Revolt in 1381?

24 The English writer Geoffrey Chaucer wrote The Canterbury Tales in 1388. Who told the tales in this work?

25 Apprenticeship spread throughout England in the 13th century. How long did an apprenticeship last before a worker became a journeyman?

1 The Sahara is the largest of the world's deserts. What is the second largest? ▼

2 Snakes do not have external ears. How do they 'hear'?

3 What is the name given to a dry stream bed that fills with water briefly after a desert storm?

4 How does a cactus plant actually survive in a desert?

5 What is a large group of locusts called?

6 A desert is an area with only a certain amount of rain per year. How much rainfall?

7 How do the large ears of animals like American jackrabbits or African fennec foxes help to keep them cool?

8 The Takla Makan desert, the 'place from which there is no return', is in which country?

9 Only around 20 per cent of the world's deserts consist of sand. What is the commoner surface?

10 What can be transverse, seif or star?

11 Which desert is the driest on earth?

12 What proportion of the land on Earth is desert?

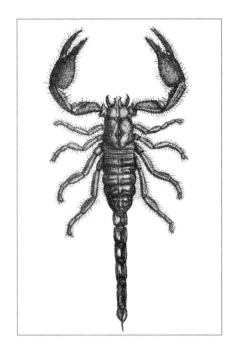

13 Which precious stones are found in the Namib desert in Africa?

14 What is the name given to flat-topped islands of rock when the face of a rock plateau is worn away?

15 Desert scorpions are dangerous creatures; how do they kill their prey? ▲

16 What type of creature is a skink?

17 In which country would you find the Simpson and Gibson deserts?

18 Out of which desert do the Hoggar (or Ahaggar) mountains rise?

19 The welwitschia plant grows where no rain has fallen for years. How does it obtain moisture?

20 What actually is the process called desertification?

21 When rock is near the surface of a desert, any water in the sand can collect and form a small area where vegetation can grow. What is such an area called?

22 Some powerful rivers run through desert areas. Which river runs through the Grand Canyon in the United States?

23 Which type of camel has two humps, the Arabian or the Bactrian?

24 How do sand dunes move?

25 In which country in the world can the Negev desert be located?

1 Who was given the nickname 'Tricky Dickie'?

2 How long is the term for which the French President is elected?

3 In 1986 the Swedish Prime Minister was shot dead as he and his wife walked home from the cinema. What was his name?

4 Which woman became Prime Minister of Pakistan in 1988 and again in 1993?

5 Who was Hitler's minister of propaganda during World War II?

6 Which British statesman spoke in 1946 of an Iron Curtain that had descended across Europe?

7 Who was leader of the Labour Party in 1983?

8 In 1979, U.S. President Jimmy Carter signed the SALT II Treaty in Vienna along with which leader?

9 Which President of Austria and former United Nations Secretary-General was accused of involvement in Nazi war atrocities?

10 Dictator Idi Amin was forced to flee his country in 1979 when Tanzanian forces invaded. What was his country?

11 Harold Wilson and Harold Macmillan were two of Britain's Prime Ministers in the 1960s. Who was the third?

12 Which country's Parliament is called Storthing?

13 Who was Mrs. Indira Gandhi's father?

14 Pierre Trudeau was Prime Minister in which country?

15 In 1981 the 'Gang of Four' left the British Labour Party to form the new Social Democratic Party. Two of them were Roy Jenkins and William Rogers. Who were the other two?

16 Which American statesman wrote his memoirs in two volumes entitled The White House Years and Years of Upheaval? ◀

17 After whose death was Prince Juan Carlos I sworn in as King of Spain? ▼

18 Which country did President Kaunda lead?

19 Name the Rhodesian Prime Minister who made the Unilateral Declaration of Independence from Britain in 1965?

20 Who prepared the blueprint for reform of America's health care system under President Clinton's administration?

21 In which European country did workers only finally obtain the right to join free trades unions in 1979?

22 Who was American Vice-President in the years 1989-93?

23 Who was Israeli Prime Minister before Yitzhak Rabin, sharing the same first name?

24 In which country was Eamonn de Valera a prominent statesman?

25 Which British journalist disappeared from Beirut and was granted asylum in the U.S.S.R. in 1963?

1 What is the name given to the killing of a brother?

2 In which film do Paul Newman and Robert Redford jump into a river holding hands?

3 3. What is the name given to a female deer?

4 Why was a young American girl, Karen Anne Quinlan, in the headlines in 1976?

5 Who gave his name to the seventh month of the year?

6 What are the names of Princess Anne's two children? ▲

7 Where would you find the Guggenheim museum?

8 What would you do with a Lee Enfield?

9 The film Gone with the Wind was based on a novel by which author? ▶

10 In Moscow, where does the Church of St. Basil stand?

11 According to the proverb, what do too many cooks do?

12 Which saint is the patron of fishermen?

13 By what name is the author H.H. Munro better known?

14 Which was the first war to be photographed?

15 In the well-known saying, 'He who can, does; he who cannot...' does what?

16 This port is known as the 'gateway to India'. What is it?

17 Which are the two smallest continents?

18 Who is considered to be the first of the classical economists?

19 What does the name Antarctica mean?

20 Which youth organization held its first jamboree in 1920?

21 Name the 23-year-old filmstar who died of suspected drug abuse in 1993.

22 Which person wrote 'a little learning is a dangerous thing'?

23 What is the actual Italian name for the great city of Venice?

24 Which zodiac sign has the symbol of the bull?

25 A religious sect, which was founded in Ireland, moved to Devon, England in 1831 and took its name from its new home. Name it.

People and Places Notable Women

1. German
2. Jane Austen
3. An escape route through Nazi occupied Europe, which ran from Brussels to the Pyrenees, that helped Allied forces escape to freedom
4. Acting
5. Jenny Lind
6. She wrote Uncle Tom's Cabin
7. 'Votes for women'
8. Russia
9. Margaret Thatcher
10. Betty Williams
11. Film actress
12. Ninette de Valois
13. Elizabeth Fry
14. Anne
15. Maria Callas
16. National Velvet
17. West Indies
18. She had a leg amputated
19. Elizabeth Garrett Anderson
20. Charlotte Corday
21. Ingrid Bergman
22. Virginia
23. Madame Curie
24. Agnes
25. Corazon Aquino

Entertaining Arts Musicals

1. My Fair Lady
2. Marvin Hamlisch
3. Rod Steiger
4. Hair
5. Call Me Madam
6. Elizabeth Taylor
7. Army nurse
8. Von Trapp
9. Jack Wild
10. Annie
11. Hammerstein
12. Victor Hugo
13. Sidney Poitier
14. Cabaret
15. Cats
16. The Philadelphia Story
17. Anna Leonowens
18. Brigadoon
19. Lerner and Loewe
20. Carousel
21. Gene Kelly
22. Eva Perón
23. Natalie Wood
24. Richard Harris
25. Debbie Reynolds

Food and Drink French cuisine

1. Clear soup with thin strips of vegetables
2. Courgettes
3. Dessert
4. Normandy
5. Biscuits
6. Bain-marie
7. Scallops
8. Maître d'hôtel
9. With finely crushed ice
10. Croque Monsieur
11. In a crust; food inside pastry
12. The first are apples, the second potatoes
13. Crêpes Suzette
14. Small cakes or biscuits
15. Egg whites
16. Plat du jour
17. Cognac
18. Main course; it is a meat and bean stew
19. Water-ice
20. Braised in red Burgundy
21. Lamb or mutton, with vegetables
22. Guide Michelin
23. Thick, batter pancake
24. Rack of lamb
25. Thick fillet of beef

Sports and Pastimes Rules of the game

1. Water-skiing
2. Bantamweight
3. Polo
4. Snatch
5. The match begins
6. Sweeping frost and moisture to clear the path for the stone
7. 12
8. Croquet
9. The forwards of each side
10. Five
11. Puck: a rubber disc used in ice hockey
12. A let
13. Seven
14. Left hand
15. Swimming, cycling and running
16. Driver
17. 35
18. Air rifle
19. 5 cm
20. Six
21. Backstroke
22. Netball
23. Four
24. Whistle
25. Rowing

History Middle Ages

1. The Danes
2. The keep
3. Charles the Great
4. Oxford
5. Scandinavia
6. Thor
7. Bayeaux tapestry
8. Jousts
9. Canterbury Cathedral
10. Palestine
11. Japan
12. Joan of Arc
13. Rebirth
14. Herbs for medicinal purposes
15. A relic of Christ or the saints
16. Wine and ale store
17. William Rufus
18. A place where guests were received
19. Florence
20. Serfs
21. Domesday Book
22. The Black Death
23. Wat Tyler
24. A group of pilgrims
25. Seven years

Natural World Deserts

1. Australian desert
2. They pick up vibrations through the ground
3. Arroyo
4. Its waxy stems expand and store water
5. A swarm
6. Less than 25 cm (10 in)
7. They lose heat from the many blood vessels close to the surface
8. China
9. Broken stone and rock
10. Sand dunes
11. Atacama desert
12. One seventh
13. Diamonds
14. Mesas
15. With the sting in their tails
16. Lizard
17. Australia
18. Southern Sahara
19. Overnight fogs leave dew on the plants
20. The expansion of deserts into areas which previously supported vegetation
21. Oasis
22. Colorado
23. Bactrian
24. Sand is blown to the top of the ridge, then trickles down the other side
25. Israel

Twentieth Century Modern Politics

1. Richard Nixon
2. Seven years
3. Olaf Palme
4. Benazir Bhutto
5. Joseph Goebbels
6. Winston Churchill
7. Neil Kinnock
8. Leonid Brezhnev
9. Kurt Waldheim
10. Uganda
11. Sir Alec Douglas-Home
12. Norway
13. Jawaharlal Nehru
14. Canada
15. Shirley Williams and David Owen
16. Henry Kissinger
17. Generalissimo Franco
18. Zambia
19. Ian Smith
20. Hillary Clinton
21. Poland
22. Dan Quayle
23. Yitzhak Shamir
24. Eire
25. H.A.R. (Kim) Philby

Pot Luck

1. Fratricide
2. Butch Cassidy and the Sundance Kid
3. Doe
4. She was in a coma and her parents fought a successful legal battle to have her removed from the respirator
5. Julius Caesar
6. Peter and Zara
7. New York
8. Shoot with it
9. Margaret Mitchell
10. Red Square
11. Spoil the broth
12. St. Peter
13. Saki
14. American Civil War
15. Teaches
16. Bombay
17. Australia and Europe
18. Adam Smith
19. Opposite the Arctic
20. Boy Scouts
21. River Phoenix
22. Alexander Pope
23. Venezia
24. Taurus
25. Plymouth Brethren

1 To which European country does the island of Madeira belong?

2 Mount Etna, the tallest volcano in Europe, stands on which island?

3 In which ocean is the area known as Polynesia?

4 The island of Taiwan is off the coast of which country?

5 Which island in the Pacific was discovered by Captain Cook in December 1777?

6 Name the island in Paris on which Notre Dame stands. ▼

7 To which group of islands does Corfu belong?

8 Which island did Turkish troops invade in 1974?

9 What is the name of the small volcanic island in the East Pacific which has some 600 strange stone statues? ▶

10 On which island are Bob Marley and Noël Coward buried?

11 The Faroes are an isolated group of islands in the North Atlantic. How many islands are there in the group?

12 Las Palmas and Santa Cruz de Tenerife are the two main groups of which islands?

13 The Zaïre (or Congo) river flows into which ocean?

14 On which island would you find the tourist resorts of Nusa Dua, Sanur and Kuta?

15 In which ocean are the islands of Mauritius and Madagascar?

16 What language is chiefly spoken by the inhabitants of what is the largest island in the Mediterranean?

17 Where was Napoleon imprisoned after his defeat at Waterloo?

18 The island of Zealand is part of which country?

19 What are the inhabitants of Sardinia called?

20 What is the world's largest island?

21 How did the Dead Sea get its name?

22 Which island country has two official languages: Sinhalese and Tamil?

23 Name the largest island belonging to Greece.

24 Where are the volcanoes Mount Erebus and Mount Terror?

25 Into which ocean does the Amazon flow?

1 An attempted assassination is the subject of *Day of the Jackal*. Who is the target?

2 The actor William Henry Pratt played the definitive monster in *Frankenstein* in 1931 and has a whole string of horror roles to his credit. Under what name is he better known?

3 In *The Omen*, an American diplomat brings up a child who is not his own. Who does the child turn out to be?

4 Name the director of *The Godfather*.

5 In which film does Popeye Doyle, played by Gene Hackman, make his debut?

6 Lycanthropy exists in the folklore of many lands and has given rise to many films. What is the popular name for a lycanthrope?

7 What character is played by Orson Welles in *The Third Man*?

8 The 1957 film *Witness for the Prosecution* was based on the play by which author?

9 Mr Hyde is the alter-ego of a respectable professional man. Who is his other half?

10 Which two actresses starred in *Whatever Happened to Baby Jane*? ▲

11 In which film did Steve McQueen star as a fire chief battling with a blaze in a skyscraper? ▶

12 Which author created the legendary vampire Count Dracula in his world famous novel published in 1897?

13 Which 1933 film told the story of a giant ape brought to New York, where it escapes and terrorizes the city before being shot down by an aircraft from the summit of the Empire State Building?

14 What was the extremely odd thing about the Stepford Wives?

15 Which male Hollywood star appeared as the Terminator?

16 Who produced, wrote the screenplay and directed *A Clockwork Orange*?

17 A 1979 film told the story of a family living in a Long Island house for a month, while they are terrorized by supernatural forces and put to flight. Where was the house?

18 Which actress starred as Rosemary in *Rosemary's Baby*?

19 *Jaws* was based on a best-selling novel by which author?

20 What type of criminals are Mel Gibson and Danny Glover chasing in *Lethal Weapon*?

21 Which film role has been played by Sean Connery, George Lazenby, Roger Moore and Timothy Dalton?

22 What event was re-told in the movie *A Night to Remember*?

23 Who starred as the villain in the remake of *Cape Fear* in 1991?

24 In which city was the atmospheric thriller *Don't Look Now* set?

25 A British star won a Best Actor Oscar in 1991 for his performance in *Silence of the Lambs*. Name him.

1 Bean sprouts are usually the sprouts of which bean?

2 Calabrese is a variety of which vegetable?

3 Americans say 'walk slowly to pick it, run back to the kitchen to cook it'. What is it?

4 Which vegetable is traditionally served with the cheese board?

5 If you were using nettles as a vegetable, how would you destroy the sting?

6 Which vegetable was regarded by the ancients as a symbol of eternity because of its many layers?

7 Laver is fried and eaten with bacon and eggs in Wales. What is it?

8 By what name is chicory better known in the United States?

9 What is often described as the 'aristocrat' of the cabbage family? ▲

10 Which type of pea can be eaten whole, including the pod?

11 Which vegetable has trench and self-blanching varieties?

12 Some vegetables contain enzymes which cause oxidation on contact with the air. What does this cause?

13 In the film starring Jessica Tandy, what was served at the Whistle Stop Café? ▶

14 What is another name for the delicious vegetable okra or bindi?

15 Which vegetable, resembling broccoli, grows wild along the seashores of northern and western Europe and is eaten like asparagus?

16 What vegetable has varieties called aquadulce, relon and red epicure?

17 The leek is the national emblem of which country?

18 What is called 'batala' in South America, 'kumara' in New Zealand and is sometimes loosely referred to as 'yams' in the United States, though yams are a different vegetable?

19 When a recipe calls for 'green beans', what would you be likely to use?

20 What is another name for the eggplant?

21 Which vegetable fruit is traditionally served in pies on the American festival of Thanksgiving?

22 Who wept in the desert as they remembered the food such as cucumbers, melons, leeks, onions and garlic?

23 Courgettes are the young version of which vegetable?

24 What is sometimes called the oyster plant or vegetable oyster?

25 Which particular type of vegetable has the name kohlrabi?

1 What is the highest number on a roulette wheel? ▼

2 What is pontoon called when it is played in a casino?

3 In the game of craps, what is the first shoot or throw of the dice called?

4 At a race meeting, what is the call over?

5 What game has suits called bamboos, characters and circles?

6 In which card game are the expressions 'for his nob' and 'for his heels' used?

7 Which American state is famous for its gambling casinos?

8 Which game is the modern version of Pope Joan, sometimes called Michigan or Saratoga in the United States and Boodle or Stops in Britain?

9 In poker, which hand is more valuable: flush or full house?

10 What is 'form' in horse-racing?

11 Which of Ian Fleming's Bond books describes the glittering world of gambling?

12 In baccarat, what is a 'natural'?

13 Keno is an American casino form of which game?

14 The 1965 film *The Cincinnati Kid* starred Edward G. Robinson and Steve McQueen. Around which card game did the film revolve? ▶

15 What is a 'straight up' bet in roulette?

16 What, in a casino, is a croupier?

17 What, in a casino, is a kibitzer?

18 In bingo, what number would a caller be giving if he said 'Key of the door'?

19 If you saw the letters 'EP' against the name of a runner on a greyhound racecard, what would it mean?

20 When playing craps, who is the 'shooter'?

21 What does it mean when a player in blackjack decides to 'stand'?

22 In the game of roulette, what is a bet on numbers 1-18 called?

23 What is the main object of the popular card game of pontoon?

24 At a race meeting, what is an 'also ran'?

25 According to the old song, all the girls used to wink an eye at 'The man who broke the bank...' where?

1. Which of the Great Train Robbers escaped from a British prison and now lives in Brazil?

2. How did Anne Bonney become notorious in the 18th century?

3. By what name is the unknown murderer who killed five women in the East End of London in 1888 remembered? ▲

4. What was the nickname of the infamous bank robber Charles Floyd, killed in a shoot-out with the FBI in 1934?

5. Which British spy, who confessed his treachery in 1964, kept his job on the Queen's payroll until he was publicly unmasked in 1978?

6. Ned Kelly, son of a convict transported to Australia from Ireland, became known in which field of crime?

7. Who is a 'fence'?

8. By what names are partners-in-crime Robert Parker and Harry Longabaugh better known?

9. Which murderer was the first to be caught by the use of ship-to-shore telegraph?

10. What was the surname of brothers Ron and Reg who ruled London's underworld for a decade and were sentenced to life imprisonment? ▶

11. When a defendant 'coughs', what does he do?

12. Forensic pathology is the investigation of what?

13. Phoolan Devi, known as the 'Beautiful Robber', was a feared bandit leader in which country?

14 Which man founded the world's famous detective agency in the United States of America in 1850?

15 Nathan Leopold and Richard Loeb killed a 14-year-old boy, Robert Franks, in Chicago in 1924. What was their motive?

16 Gangster Al Capone, boss of the Chicago underworld, was finally gaoled for 11 years for what crime?

17 Vlad V of Transylvania, the original 'Dracula', was a sadistic killer who drank the blood of his victims. His method of killing earned him what grim nickname?

18 In 1932, the Lindbergh baby was kidnapped and killed. For what was his father Colonel Charles Lindbergh famous?

19 What is toxicology?

20 Name the notorious pair of bodysnatchers who robbed graves in Scotland in the 1820s to sell bodies for dissection, and later murdered at least 15 people?

21 The science of ballistics is concerned with what?

22 What is the method of identification that uses the genetic material from our cells to produce a virtually unique pattern or 'fingerprint' called?

23 Madeleine Smith was tried for the murder by poison of her lover in Edinburgh in 1857. What was the verdict?

24 The 15th century Cesare Borgia was an expert in which type of killing?

25 Which woman thief and bank robber later reformed and became a society columnist in New York and was eventually murdered in her own home by burglars in 1924?

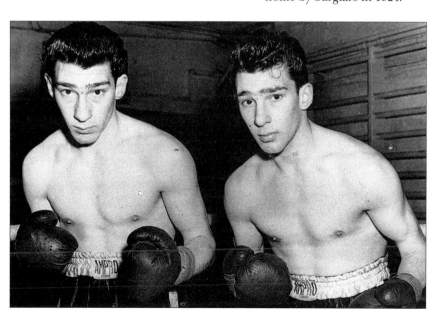

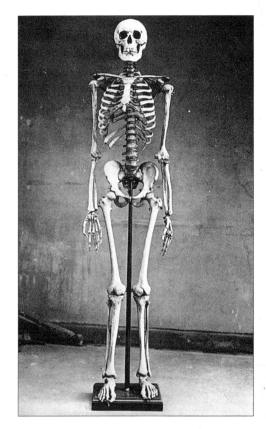

1 Which organ of the body is affected if someone is suffering from Bright's disease?

2 Where did the 'funny-bone' get its nickname?

3 Blood is classified in four main groups. A, B, and AB are three of them; what is the fourth?

4 Shallow sleep, which is the time when we dream, is also known as REM sleep. What does REM stand for?

5 What are the phalanges?

6 Muscles account for what percentage of total body weight?

7 How many litres of blood are contained in an adult's body?

8 The top bone of the backbone is called the atlas bone, after the Greek god Atlas. In legend, what did Atlas do?

9 What is the normal body temperature?

10 How many separate bones are there in the body of an adult? ▲

11 Which side of the brain governs creative skills?

12 What colour eyes is a baby likely to have if one parent has blue eyes and the other brown?

13 The retina of the eye has light-sensitive nerve cells called rods and cones. Which of these enable us to see colour?

14 Which gland in the body secretes the hormone responsible for growth?

15 What does the abbreviation IVF stand for?

16 Where would you find the coccyx?

17 Most people are right– or left-handed but what word describes those who can use either hand with equal ease?

18 What is the common name for the scapula?

19 Identical twins come from a single fertilized egg which splits in two; non-identical twins come from two fertilized eggs. What are non-identical twins called? ▼

20 Where would you find the femur in the human body?

21 What is the world's commonest contagious disease?

22 Give the scientific name for the jawbone.

23 What particular name is given to the study of character by feeling the lumps and bumps of the head?

24 What is a specialist in skin disorders called?

25 Hairs grow out of pits in the skin. What are these pits called?

1 What made Christiaan Barnard of Cape Town famous in 1967?

2 Rhodesia, in 1964, declared UDI. What does UDI stand for?

3 The first Bond movie was released in 1962. What was the title?

4 What device, aimed at cutting drink–driving accidents, was introduced in Britain in October 1967?

5 What were the proprietary names of the widely prescribed tranquillizing drug diazepam, first used in the 1960s?

6 'The eagle has landed' reported Edward (Buzz) Aldrin in July 1969. What was he talking about?

7 Who killed American Civil Rights leader Martin Luther King in 1968?

8 Which of London's streets became famous with fashion-conscious youngsters throughout the world?

9 Ho Chi Minh, who led the independence struggle against the French, was the first president of which country?

10 In the 1960s the Beatles were among the followers of Maharishi Mahesh Yogi. What technique did he teach?

11 Muhammed Ali was professional world heavyweight champion 1964-67. What was his catch-phrase?

12 The Cockney model Twiggy was one of the top models of the 1960s. What was her real name? ◀

13 Who was the star with the wholesome and feminine image who proved a big box office draw in films like *The Thrill of it All* and *Move over Darling*?

14 What was the name of the group put together especially for a TV series as an American answer to the Beatles and which achieved a surprising level of success?

15 Who was the captain of the spaceship that went where 'no man has gone before'?

16 In 1960 South African police fired on an anti-apartheid demonstration killing 56 and injuring 162. Where did this massacre take place?

17 What was held at Woodstock, New York, in 1969?

18 What style of hat did Jackie Kennedy wear for her husband's inauguration ceremony that set a new fashion trend?

19 With which fashion style was British designer Mary Quant associated?

20 American Professor Timothy Leary, author of *The Politics of Ecstasy* claimed that a psychedelic drug could enhance the spiritual quality of life. Which drug?

21 What was the title of the first Beatles' single? ▲

22 *Barbarella*, a space fantasy based on a comic strip, helped to inspire fashions like cat-suits and high boots for some years to come. Who starred as Barbarella?

23 At the 1968 Olympics in Mexico, several American medal-winning black athletes rebelled during the playing of their national anthem. What did they do?

24 Who fought the Six Day War in 1967?

25 Name the American exponent of 'pop art' who used ordinary objects, such as soup cans and soap packets, in his creations.

1 The picture of which American President appears on the one dollar bill?

2 Which musician was known as 'the king of swing'?

3 Name the silent screen comedian who was writer, director and star of *The Navigator*?

4 The Hare Krishna sect is an orthodox exponent of which religion?

5 If a government claims that it has a mandate from the electorate, what does it mean?

6 With which sport is William 'the Refrigerator' Perry associated?

7 U Thant was the Secretary General of the UN from 1962 to 1971. What was his home country?

8 Which planet is known as the 'red planet'?

9 In 1957, the first black player won the ladies' singles title at Wimbledon. Name her. ◀ ▶

10 Blanket and honeycomb are the two main types of what?

11 In the rhyme about birthdays, a child born on which day is said to be 'full of grace'?

12 Which English city exports cutlery all over the world?

13 The bite of which insect can spread sleeping sickness?

14 What would you do with a *dhoti*?

15 'Mayday' is the word used as a distress signal. Where does the word come from?

16 Which writer wrote *Jude the Obscure* and *Return of the Native*?

17 On which day of the year are hot cross buns traditionally eaten?

18 Which series of 15th–century wars ended with the battle of Bosworth Field?

19 What happened to British Prime Minister Spencer Perceval in May, 1812?

20 What instrument does Ravi Shankar play?

21 To which royal house did Marie Antoinette belong?

22 On which book was the musical *Cabaret* based?

23 Roald Dahl wrote the book called *BFG*. What do the initials stand for?

24 According to the song, what did Molly Malone sell on the streets of Dublin?

25 Whose seaplane was called *The Spruce Goose*?

People and Places Seas and Islands

1. Portugal
2. Sicily
3. Pacific
4. China
5. Christmas Island
6. Ile de la Cité
7. Ionian Islands
8. Cyprus
9. Easter Island
10. Jamaica
11. 18
12. Canary Islands
13. Atlantic
14. Bali
15. Indian
16. Italian; the island is Sicily
17. St. Helena
18. Denmark
19. Sards
20. Greenland
21. The salt content is so high that no vegetation can live there
22. Sri Lanka
23. Crete
24. On Ross Island in Antarctica
25. Atlantic

Entertaining Arts Screen Thrills

1. General de Gaulle
2. Boris Karloff
3. The Anti-Christ
4. Francis Ford Coppola
5. The French Connection
6. Werewolf
7. Harry Lime
8. Agatha Christie
9. Dr. Jekyll
10. Bette Davis and Joan Crawford
11. The Towering Inferno
12. Bram Stoker
13. King Kong
14. They were robots
15. Arnold Schwarzenegger
16. Stanley Kubrick
17. Amityville
18. Mia Farrow
19. Peter Benchley
20. Drug dealers
21. James Bond
22. Sinking of the Titanic
23. Robert de Niro
24. Venice
25. Anthony Hopkins

Food and Drink Vegtables

1. Mung beans
2. Broccoli
3. Sweetcorn
4. Celery
5. Cook them
6. Onions
7. Seaweed
8. Endive
9. Cauliflower
10. Mangetout or sugar peas
11. Celery
12. Discoloration
13. Fried green tomatoes
14. Ladies' fingers
15. Seakale
16. Broad beans
17. Wales
18. Sweet potato
19. French or runner beans
20. Aubergine
21. Pumpkin
22. Children of Israel after leaving Egypt
23. Marrow
24. Salsify
25. Cabbage

Sports and Pastimes Betting and Gaming

1. 36
2. Blackjack
3. The comeout
4. Naming of horses with the latest betting odds
5. Mah jong
6. Cribbage
7. Nevada
8. Newmarket
9. Full house
10. The record of performance of what a horse has and has not achieved
11. Casino Royale
12. A score of 8 or 9 with two cards
13. Bingo
14. Stud poker
15. A bet on a single number
16. An employee who runs the game
17. An onlooker
18. 21
19. Early pace
20. The first person to throw the dice
21. The player takes no more cards
22. Manque
23. To score 21 or as near as possible
24. A horse that has finished out of the money
25. Monte Carlo

History Crime and Criminals

1. Ronnie Biggs
2. She was a pirate
3. Jack the Ripper
4. Pretty Boy
5. Anthony Blunt
6. Bank robbery
7. Someone who sells stolen goods on behalf of thieves
8. Butch Cassidy and the Sundance Kid
9. Dr. Crippin
10. Kray
11. Confesses
12. Suspicious or criminal causes of death or injury
13. India
14. Alan Pinkerton
15. Thrills
16. Tax evasion
17. Vlad the Impaler
18. The first non-stop transatlantic flight
19. Study of poisons
20. Burke and Hare
21. Firearms
22. DNA profiling
23. Not proven
24. Poisoning
25. Sophie Lyons

Natural World The Human Body

1. Kidney
2. From the scientific name, the 'humerus'
3. O
4. Rapid Eye Movement
5. Finger and toe bones
6. 40 per cent
7. Over 4.5 litres
8. Supported the world on his shoulders
9. 37° C (98.6° F)
10. 206
11. Left
12. Brown
13. Cones
14. Pituitary
15. In vitro fertilization
16. The lower end of the spinal column
17. Ambidextrous
18. Shoulder blade
19. Fraternal
20. The thigh
21. Common cold
22. Mandible
23. Phrenology
24. Dermatologist
25. Follicles

Twentieth Century The 1960s

1. He performed the first heart transplant
2. Unilateral Declaration of Independence
3. Dr. No
4. Breathalyzer
5. Valium and Librium
6. The first moon landing
7. James Earl Ray
8. Carnaby Street
9. North Vietnam
10. Transcendental Meditation
11. 'I am the greatest'
12. Lesley Hornby
13. Doris Day
14. The Monkees
15. James Kirk
16. Sharpeville
17. Rock festival
18. Pill-box
19. Mini-skirt
20. LSD
21. Love Me Do
22. Jane Fonda
23. They gave a clenched fist 'black power' salute
24. Arabs and Israelis
25. Andy Warhol

Pot Luck

1. George Washington
2. Benny Goodman
3. Buster Keaton
4. Hinduism
5. It has the authority to carry out certain policies
6. American football
7. Burma
8. Mars
9. Althea Gibson
10. Tripe
11. Tuesday
12. Sheffield
13. Tsetse fly
14. Wear it
15. From the French m'aidez, meaning 'help me'
16. Thomas Hardy
17. Good Friday
18. Wars of the Roses
19. He was assassinated
20. Sitar
21. Hapsburg
22. I am a Camera by Christopher Isherwood
23. Big Friendly Giant
24. Cockles and mussels
25. Howard Hughes

Quiz

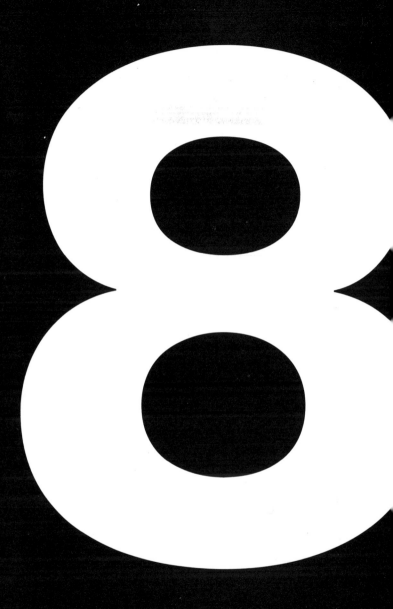

1. What, in New York City, is known as the lungs of the city?

2. Which country is the leading world producer of tobacco?

3. Before it was bought by the United States in 1867, which country owned Alaska?

4. In which cemetery, just outside Washington DC, have soldiers been buried since American the Civil War?

5. The Spanish explorer Ponce de Leon discovered Florida in 1513. What was he seeking at the time?

6. Texas, Idaho and Oklahoma all have panhandles. What are they?

7. What is the language of Uruguay?

8. President Alfonsin was ruler in which South American country?

9 In the United States, Thanksgiving Day is celebrated each November. Why did the early settlers begin the festival?

10 The New Orleans festival of Mardi Gras, with its parades, floats and general revelry, is world famous. When does it take place? ▶

11 Which city in Tennessee is known as the home of country music?

12 Who are the Dallas Cowboys?

13 What unit of currency is used in the country of Bolivia?

14 Which city in Michigan, United States, is known as Motor City because of the large number of cars built there?

15 For what crop is the Napa Valley in California best known?

16 Which South American country has the world's highest cable car?

17 The Astrodome in Houston, United States, was the first air-conditioned indoor stadium in the world. What is played there?

18 Which legendary film director made several westerns, including *Stagecoach*, in Monument Valley, Utah?

19 What is the official language of Surinam?

20 Which famous university is located in Cambridge, Massachusetts?

21 Yellowstone National Park, in the northern United States, is famous for springs that spout boiling water and steam. What are they called? ◀

22 Olympia is the capital of which American state?

23 The world's second longest river flows through South America. Name it.

24 One of the largest sculptures in the world, showing the heads of four presidents, is at Mount Rushmore in South Dakota. Three of them are George Washington, Thomas Jefferson and Abraham Lincoln. Who is the fourth?

25 The harbour of which South American city is dominated by the Sugar Loaf and Corcovado mountains?

1 Which silent movie actress, known as 'America's Sweetheart', later became Vice-President of United Artists?

2 Who played Eliza in *My Fair Lady* on Broadway only to lose the role to Audrey Hepburn in the film?

3 How was Elizabeth Taylor's husband, film producer Mike Todd, killed in 1958?

4 For which flamboyant actress did Noël Coward write *Private Lives*? ▲

5 Name the two actress daughters of John Mills.

6 Ingrid Bergman won Best Actress Oscars for *Gaslight* and *Anastasia*. In 1974 she won a Best Supporting Actress award for a role in which film? ▶

7 Which child actress played opposite her father in *Paper Moon*?

8 Who took a year off after filming *Hook*, then married Lyle Lovett and signed a multi-million dollar contract to film a Gothic horror tale *Mary Reilly*?

9 Which actress won a coveted role in a blockbuster picture when she arrived on the set to watch a city burn?

10 Who was nominated as Best Actress for her first film *The Color Purple* in 1985?

11 Judy Garland's daughter became a famous singer and actress. Name her.

12 In which 1989 film did Pauline Collins play a middle-aged woman who goes to Greece to find adventure?

13 When Winston Churchill saw *Mrs Miniver* he said that it would prove more valuable for the war effort than the combined efforts of six divisions. Who played Mrs Miniver?

14 Which singer did Sissy Spacek play in *Coal Miner's Daughter*?

15 How was Norma Jean Baker better known in public life?

16 Which 93-year-old actress played opposite Bette Davis in *The Whales of August*?

17 Name the established Broadway star who made her home at London's Savoy Hotel for some years and was a great success in the TV series *Two's Company* with Donald Sinden, before returning to the United States in 1982?

18 How is Mrs. Charles Black better known?

19 Who plays the mute wife in an arranged marriage in *The Piano*?

20 Which leading lady has written several books on reincarnation?

21 In *The Avengers*, Honor Blackman and Diana Rigg both played John Steed's side-kick. Which actress appeared in *New Avengers*?

22 Who won her fourth Tony award in 1979 for her performance in Sondheim's *Sweeney Todd* and is now better known as a TV sleuth?

23 Which young actress played a juvenile prostitute at the age of 14 and later played the victim of a gang rape?

24 Jean Marsh was one of the originators of the TV series *Upstairs Downstairs*. What role did she play in the series?

25 Who lodged in an L-shaped room and danced with puppets in *Lili*?

1 Name the delicacy made from the liver of specially fattened geese.

2 What is the usual name for the alligator pear?.

3 At what particular stage of a meal is a *bombe* usually served?

4 Which type of fish is known as an Arbroath smokey?

5 What is the meaning of *rijstaffel*, a banquet with up to 25 dishes?

6 What type of fruit is a kumquat?

7 Stilton, known in Britain as the 'king of cheeses' is traditionally served with which drink?

8 What are the fungi used in gourmet cooking and found growing wild among tree roots mainly in France and Italy?

9 If you were eating fish 'a la Normande', how would the fish be cooked?

10 In Japanese cooking, why must the chef be very careful when preparing the globe fish, *fugu*? ▲

11 What is the main ingredient of the dish called 'angels on horseback'?

12 From which fish does caviar come?

13 What is the world's most expensive spice?

14 The Italian name is scampi and this is often used on international restaurant menus, but what is the English name?

15 What type of food is 'bouillabaisse'?

16 What is the name given to poached and glazed chestnuts?

17 Which fruit is often served with Parma ham as a first course?

18 What is the 'glorious twelfth'?

19 What is the main ingredient of Tía Maria liqueur?

20 From which country do the cheeses Marscarpone, Ricotta and Provolone come?

21 What type of oven, used to cook marinated meat, is a tandoor?

22 Beef stroganoff was first made in the 1700s for Count Alexander Stroganoff. After the meat is cooked, what is added?

23 What do we call young herring and sprats, when coated in flour and deep-fried until crisp and golden-brown?

24 What are the main ingredients of hollandaise sauce?

25 Pheasants are now found all over the northern hemisphere, but what is their native country? ▼

1. The first woman to run a mile in under five minutes was Diane Leather. What nationality was she?

2. How many spikes do the shoes of discus and hammer throwers have?

3. How many spikes do the shoes of contestants in the javelin event have?

4. For how many years did Jesse Owens' long jump record, set in 1935, stand? ▶ ▶

5. Which British athlete won every decathlon he entered between 1979 and 1984 and was known for his rivalry with Germany's Jurgen Hingsen?

6. If the baton is dropped as it is changing hands in a relay race, who must pick it up?

7. Serge Bubka has broken 29 outdoor and indoor records in pole vaulting. Which country does he represent?

8. The Marathon commemorates the run of a courier who took the news of the victory over the Persians from Marathon to which city?

9. Kenyan athlete Ibrahim Hussain won which marathon in 1991 and 1992?

10. What is a heat?

11. In which event might a competitor use the 'Fosbury Flop'?

12. How many obstacles would you find in the 110 metres hurdles event?

13. In which athletic event do the contestants aim to move only backwards?

14. What is the venue for the 1994 Commonwealth Games?

15. Who was the first British athlete to set a world record in a field event when she set a new javelin world record in 1986?

16. In which field event did Brazil's Adhemar Ferreira da Silva win every title from 1951 to 1959?

17. Who won the 1960 Olympic Marathon, running without shoes?

18. In running events, what is a break?

19 19. What is the scratch line?

20 Ed Moses of the United States is one of the legendary champions of track and field. In which event was he twice Olympic Champion?

21 What is the largest number of Olympic gold medals in athletics to be won by a woman?

22 The only walker to win three Olympic gold medals was Ugo Frigerio. Which country did he represent?

23 What close relation is gold medal winner Jackie Joyner-Kersee to the great athlete Florence Griffith-Joyner?

24 In what class of athletic events have Steve Ovett, Sebastian Coe and Steve Cram achieved fame?

25 The American Mary Decker-Slaney claimed that she had been tripped by another athlete when running in the 1984 Olympics. Who was that athlete?

1 Which famous bridge stands at the entrance to San Francisco Bay?

2 Name the building that stood as the centrepiece of the Paris Exhibition of 1899 and for 40 years was the world's tallest man-made edifice?

3 Which is the only one of the seven wonders of the ancient world to survive?

4 What is the world's largest amusement park?

5 What is the name of the arena in Rome which was the site of gladiatorial contests and Christian martyrdom?

6 Which Australian city is famous for the Opera House and the Harbour Bridge? ▲

7 What great engineering feat was completed in 1914, providing a short route for shipping between the Atlantic and Pacific oceans?

8 The tallest building in the world is the Sears tower. In which American city does it stand?

9 What would you find in Gorëme, in the Turkish region of Cappadocia?

10 Which French king built the palace of Versailles outside Paris, its splendour becoming famous throughout Europe?

11 What is the name of the 'lost' city of the Incas, in Peru, which was rediscovered by Hiram Bingham in 1911?

12 What is the only man-made structure on Earth which is visible from the moon?

13 The Tower of London began with a fortress built by William the Conqueror. What is the oldest structure within the Tower? ▶

14 For what purpose was the Taj Mahal built by Mogul Emperor Shah Jahan?

15 In 1974 farm labourers in China were drilling a well when they discovered a large collection of life-size figures. What are they called?

16 For what is the Sistine Chapel chiefly famous?

17 Name the massive prehistoric stone circle which stands in the middle of England's Salisbury Plain.

18 The famous Egyptian rock temples built in honour of Rameses II were dismantled and reassembled at a new site when the Aswan dam was built. By what name are the temples known?

19 What famous classical site, once a stronghold of the Athenian kings, stands on a rocky outcrop above Athens?

20 The world's largest concrete dam stands on the Columbia River in Washington state, United States. What is it called?

21 What is the height, in feet, of St. Paul's Cathedral in London?

22 Where in St. Petersburg is the Hermitage art collection housed?

23 The world's largest telescope is on the volcano Mauna Kea. Where is the volcano?

24 Which of the seven wonders of the ancient world stood in Ephesus?

25 What splendid building stands in Jerusalem, on the spot from which Mohammed was said to have ascended to heaven?

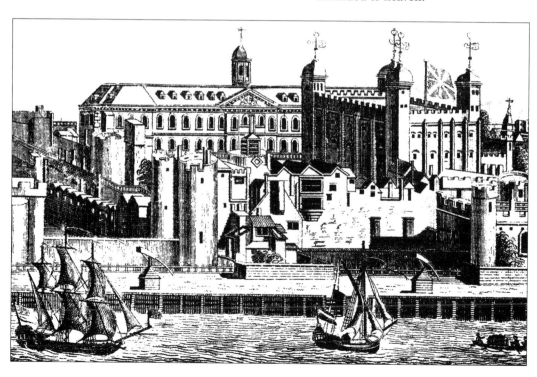

1 Where is the largest of the world's rainforests?

2 Elephants and buffaloes are herbivores. What does this mean they feed on? ▼

3 To which family of animals does the ocelot belong?

4 Twenty per cent of all drugs contain extracts of rainforest plants. From what does the malaria drug quinine derive?

5 What do scientists call plants or animals that are studied to check the health of a particular environment?

6 What particular type of animal is the very agile tree-climbing tamandua from South America?

7 What is the other name for the animal known as the flying fox (so called because of its fox-like face) which feeds on fruits such as figs, bananas, mangoes, etc.?

8 Why does the Australian animal the koala not need to drink?

9 How does the male cricket attract a mate?

10 What type of plants are epiphytes?

11 Which is the largest of the tree-dwelling apes, whose name means 'forest man'?

12 What are the proper names for male and female badgers?

13 Which is the world's biggest deer?

14 If you were escaping from an angry black bear, could you do this by climbing a tree?

15 From what part of the oil palm tree is the oil used to make soap, margarine and candles taken?

16 Why is the Midwife Toad so–called?

17 What is the annual rainfall of the 'rainforest'?

18 What purpose do the vivid orange and black stripes of the tiger centipede fulfil?

19 What is the principal food of the giant panda? ▲

20 Which Australian bird is often called the 'alarm bird' or 'breakfast bird' because its call is particularly loud in the morning?

21 What is the dominant feature of the pot-bellied, tree-living proboscis monkey?

22 What is the largest parrot in the rainforest?

23 What substance, taken from forest trees, goes into the making of rubber?

24 Where is the largest tropical forest in Africa?

25 The skin on the throat of a frog can expand like a balloon for what purpose?

1 With which charity is Princess Anne particularly associated?

2 How old was Princess Elizabeth when she became Queen? ▲

3 The Duke and Duchess of York married in Westminster Abbey. Where did the Prince and Princess of Wales marry?

4 Whom did Princess Margaret marry in 1960?

5 Which are the two private residences of Queen Elizabeth II?

6 At which university did Prince Charles read archaeology and anthropology?

7 Which member of the British royal family did Baroness Marie Christine von Reibnitz become on her marriage?

8 How did Michael Fagan come into contact with the royal family in 1982?

9 Which male member of the royal family served with the Royal Navy in the Falklands war against Argentina?

10 Who wrote the children's story *The Old Man of Lochnagar*?

11 Who was the governess to Princess Elizabeth and Princess Margaret who angered the royal family by publishing a book of reminiscences when she left royal service?

12 What is the name of the 18th–century mansion bought by the Queen as a home for the newly married Princess Anne and Captain Mark Philips in 1976?

13 Which major anniversary did the Queen celebrate in 1977?

14 Which of the Queen's children was the first royal baby to be born at Buckingham Palace for 62 years?

15 Which royal wife's jewellery was auctioned at Sotheby's in 1987?

16 What was the Duchess of Kent's maiden name?

17 Which designers created Lady Diana Spencer's wedding dress? ▼

18 Where did the investiture of Prince Charles as Prince of Wales take place in 1969?

19 Which sport did the Duke of Edinburgh take up when he retired from polo?

20 What was Elizabeth the Queen Mother's maiden name?

21 What connection has London-born Jeannette Charles with the royal family?

22 In which year did Princess Anne compete in Great Britain's equestrian team in the Olympics Games?

23 Whose daughter is Lady Helen Windsor?

24 Name the Duke of York's two children.

25 Who is third in line of succession to the throne?

1 Whose biography is called *Waxmaker Extraordinary?*

2 Walter Mondale was appointed to which office by President Clinton in 1993? ▼

3 What is the capital of Turkey?

4 In which country are the ruins of the city of Carthage situated?

5 Who said that 'in the future everyone will be famous for 15 minutes'?

6 Which part of the eye determines its colour?

7 Who followed Charles de Gaulle as President of France in 1969? ▶

8 Trichology is the study of what?

9 In *Hamlet*, Polonius is stabbed behind an arras. What is an arras?

10 In the Morse code, which letter is indicated by one dash?

11 To what was the Trojan prophetess Cassandra doomed?

12 Which bird lays the smallest egg?

13 Who retired after four years as Chairman of United States Joint Chiefs of Staff in September 1993?

14 Who wrote *The Tale of Peter Rabbit?*

15 What is a crack in a glacier called?

16 In the British Parliament, who sits on the Woolsack in the House of Lords?

17 Paul McCartney has always used his middle name. What is his first name?

18 Which stunning film actress, daughter of a famous father had children by Roger Vadim and Marcello Mastroianni without being married to either of them at the time?

19 In Britain, how many old pennies made up a 'tanner'?

20 The instruments which make up the brass section of the orchestra are trombone, trumpet, tuba and which other instrument?

21 Who is the patron saint of children?

22 Where would you find the medieval illuminated manuscript the *Book of Kells*?

23 Which American city is nicknamed the 'Windy City'?

24 Name the 1988 film that told the story of the trial of Stephen Ward and the Profumo affair?

25 How long must a dog arriving in Britain from abroad spend in quarantine?

People and Places   The Americas

1. Central Park
2. Brazil
3. Russia
4. Arlington Cemetery
5. The fountain of youth
6. Strips of land stretching into another state
7. Spanish
8. Argentina
9. To celebrate their first harvest
10. Shrove Tuesday
11. Nashville
12. American football team
13. Peso
14. Detroit
15. Grapes
16. Venezuela
17. Baseball and American football
18. John Ford
19. Dutch
20. Harvard
21. Geysers
22. Washington
23. Amazon
24. Theodore Roosevelt
25. Rio de Janeiro

Entertaining Arts   Leading Ladies

1. Mary Pickford
2. Julie Andrews
3. Plane crash
4. Gertrude Lawrence
5. Hayley and Juliet
6. Murder on the Orient Express
7. Tatum O'Neal
8. Julia Roberts
9. Vivien Leigh in Gone with the Wind
10. Whoopi Goldberg
11. Liza Minnelli
12. Shirley Valentine
13. Greer Garson
14. Loretta Lynn
15. Marilyn Monroe
16. Lillian Gish
17. Elaine Stritch
18. Shirley Temple
19. Holly Hunter
20. Shirley MacLean
21. Joanna Lumley
22. Angela Lansbury
23. Jodie Foster
24. The maid, Rose
25. Leslie Caron

Food and Drink   Gourmet Fare

1. Pâté de foie gras
2. Avocado pear
3. Dessert
4. Haddock
5. Rice table
6. Orange
7. Port
8. Truffles
9. Braised in white wine
10. The flesh is poisonous – some parts more than others
11. Oysters
12. Sturgeon
13. Saffron
14. Dublin Bay Prawns
15. Fish stew
16. Marrons glacés
17. Melon
18. The beginning of the grouse-shooting season – August 12
19. Coffee beans
20. Italy
21. A charcoal-fired clay oven
22. Sour cream
23. Whitebait
24. Butter and egg yolks
25. China

Sports and Pastimes   Athletics

1. British
2. None
3. A maximum of 11
4. 25 years
5. Daley Thompson
6. The runner who dropped it
7. U.S.S.R., now C.I.S
8. Athens
9. Boston
10. A preliminary round
11. High jump
12. 10
13. Tug of war
14. Victoria, Canada
15. Fatima Whitbread
16. Triple jump
17. Abebe Bikila
18. When a runner establishes a gap between himself and the other competitors
19. The line an athlete must not cross at the end of the runway for the javelin, long jump and triple jump events
20. Hurdles
21. Four
22. Italy
23. Sister-in-law
24. Middle distance running
25. Zola Budd

History   Man-made Wonders

1. Golden Gate Bridge
2. Eiffel Tower
3. The pyramids of Giza
4. Disney World, Florida
5. Colosseum
6. Sydney
7. Panama Canal
8. Chicago
9. Rock temples with frescoes
10. Louis XIV
11. Machu Picchu
12. Great Wall of China
13. White Tower
14. A mausoleum for his wife
15. Terracotta warriors of Xi'an
16. Frescoes by Michelangelo
17. Stonehenge
18. Abu Simbel
19. Acropolis
20. Grand Coulee
21. 365
22. The Winter Palace
23. Hawaii
24. Temple of Artemis
25. Dome of the Rock

Natural World   Woods and Forests

1. Amazon basin
2. Plants
3. Cats
4. Tree bark
5. Indicator species
6. Anteater
7. Fruit bat
8. It obtains sufficient moisture from eucalyptus leaves
9. It stridulates (rubs parts of its body together to make a shrill sound)
10. They live on other plants but do not damage them
11. Orangutan
12. Boar and sow
13. Moose
14. No; they can climb
15. The fruit
16. The male carries the eggs on its hind legs
17. 300-600 cm (120-240 in)
18. They warn enemies that it is poisonous
19. Bamboo shoots
20. Kookaburra
21. A huge, bulbous nose
22. Macaw
23. A milky white juice called latex
24. Congo Basin
25. To make its mating call louder

Twentieth Century   British Royals

1. Save the Children Fund
2. 25
3. St. Paul's Cathedral
4. Antony Armstrong-Jones
5. Balmoral and Sandringham
6. Cambridge
7. Princess Michael of Kent
8. He managed to get into the Queen's bedroom in Buckingham Palace
9. Prince Andrew
10. Prince Charles
11. Marion Crawford (Crawfie)
12. Gatcombe Park
13. Silver Jubilee
14. Prince Charles
15. Duchess of Windsor
16. Katharine Worsley
17. Elizabeth and David Emanuel
18. Caernarfon Castle
19. Carriage driving
20. Bowes-Lyon
21. She has made a career out of being the Queen's look-alike
22. 1976
23. Duke and Duchess of Kent
24. Beatrice and Eugenie
25. Prince Henry

Pot Luck

1. Madame Tussaud's
2. Ambassador to Japan
3. Ankara
4. Tunisia
5. Andy Warhol
6. The iris
7. Georges Pompidou
8. Hair and scalp
9. A wall hanging
10. T
11. To tell the truth and never be believed
12. Bee hummingbird (0.35 cm/1/4 inch long)
13. General Colin Powell
14. Beatrix Potter
15. Crevasse
16. Lord Chancellor
17. James
18. Catherine Deneuve
19. Six
20. Horn
21. St. Nicholas
22. Trinity College, Dublin
23. Chicago
24. Scandal
25. Six months

Quiz

1. What is the world's most southerly capital?

2. In Jerusalem, what important Jewish memorial is the last remaining part of the Jewish temple built by Herod?

3. What is housed in the Prado, Madrid?

4. Columbo is the capital of which Commonwealth country?

5. Which building in Moscow has a name meaning 'citadel'?

6. Honolulu is the capital of the state of Hawaii. What is the name of its famous beach?

7. In Paris, what name is given to the artists' and writers' quarter?

8. How long was the original lease of Hong Kong from China, that ends in 1997?

9. Name the Lebanese capital which reduced to anarchy in the 1980s as factions fought for supremacy?

10. In London it is called the tube or the underground. What is it called in Paris?

11. Which country has Vaduz as its capital?

12. In which capital city is the Humboldt University, the Brandenburg Gate and the Kaiser Wilhelm Memorial Church? ▲

13. On the island of Malta, Valetta is the capital but what is the largest and most modern city?

14. Where would you find the Tivoli Pleasure Gardens?

15. What is the world's highest capital city?

16. Oscar Wilde died and was buried in which city?

17 Washington DC, named after George Washington, is the capital of the United States. What does DC stand for?

18 In which city would you walk through the Gate of Heavenly Peace and find yourself in front of the monument to the People's Heroes?

19 Name the capital city of Zambia.

20 In which city could you travel on the Chao Phraya river to see Wat Po and the Wat Arun?

21 What is the world's northernmost capital?

22 On which river do the cities of Vienna, Budapest and Belgrade stand?

23 The Trevi fountain is one of Rome's tourist attractions. What is promised to any visitor who throws a coin into the fountain? ▼

24 In which city are the headquarters of the Arab League?

25 Which European city is the headquarters of Sabena World Airlines?

1 Who played Count Dracula most times on film?

2 Which 'hero of Arabia' had appalling notices for his Macbeth on the London stage and resigned from the board of the Old Vic when the directors disowned the production?

3 For which film, the last before his death, did Henry Fonda achieve an Oscar?

4 Zero Mostel played the lead role in Fiddler on the Roof on Broadway. Who took over the film role?

5 Who is Bernard Schwartz?

6 Which screen star had his feet insured for $150,000?

7 John Wayne, receiving an Oscar after 42 years in the business, said 'If I'd known, I'd have put the eyepatch on 35 years earlier'. What film was he talking about? ◀

8 Which actor is married to Joanne Woodward?

9 Who played the bogus instrument salesman in The Music Man on Broadway and on the screen?

10 Which filmstar became Mayor of Carmel?

11 In which musical did Laurence Olivier take a singing role?

12 Which actor dressed as a woman in one movie and played an autistic savant in another?

13 In 1946, Humphrey Bogart played Philip Marlowe in The Big Sleep. Who took the role in the 1978 version?

14 Which star of Brighton Rock and Morning Departure went on to direct Oh What a Lovely War and Young Winston?

15 Name Steve McQueen's last film?

16 Who refused his Academy Award for his role in Patton?

17 Which actor, who founded the Mercury Theater and directed Citizen Kane, later took to voice-overs on TV commercials?

18 In Reversal of Fortune the actor Jeremy Irons played a multi-millionaire tried for the attempted murder of his wife.
Who was he actually playing? ▶

19 Which famous Hollywood actor, once, remarkably, a circus acrobat, played a king on Broadway for 1,246 performances and then revived the role in 1972?

20 Which famous British wit, in the famous song, advised Mrs. Worthington not to put her daughter on the stage?

21 In which two films did Marlon Brando win an Oscar?

22 Whose Indian name was Dances with Wolves in the 1990 film?

23 Which Welsh miner's son starred as the Archbishop of Canterbury in Becket?

24 Who was catapulted to stardom in Alfie?

25 By what name is John Carter better known?

1 The French call it sabayon. What do the Italians call it?

2 If you ordered Cherries Jubilee, how would you expect them to be cooked?

3 What name is given to a custard whisked with gelatine, with whipped cream added?

4 A Linzer torte, named after an Austrian town, has a ground nut pastry base spread with jam. What type of topping does it have?

5 On the dessert menu, what is a compôte?

6 What type of pastry is used for profiteroles?

7 What type of pastry is used for jam roly-poly?

8 For what was liquorice used in ancient Egypt?

9 Halva is made from sugar, water, butter, nuts and what else?

10 The Australian biscuits called Anzac biscuits, containing rolled oats and golden syrup, got their name in World War I. Where did the name come from?

11 What colour is the pistachio nut, often used in ice cream and confectionery?

12 Marshmallows are now made from sugar, egg white and gelatine. From what were they made originally?

13 Crème brûlée is a rich custard topped with sugar. How is the topping prepared?

14 The root of sarsaparilla, a plant native to South America, is used to flavour confectionery, desserts and drinks. What flavour is it?

15 Baked Alaska has meringue on the outside. What does the meringue cover?

16 What sweet can be made from the sap of the South American sapodilla tree?

17 Banbury cakes come from a town in the Midlands of England. The sweet pastry has what kind of filling?

18 What food has a name that means 'baked twice'?

19 Baklava, a Middle Eastern pastry, has layers of buttered filo pastry with chopped nuts, sugar and cinnamon. What process does it undergo after cooking?

20 What type of sweets did American President Reagan have on his desk?

21 How does the French cake dessert millefeuille get its name?

22 What name is given to sweetened cream beaten to the consistency of a mousse, sometimes flavoured with vanilla?

23 Which German chocolate cake with a filling of cherries, cream and kirsch, has become internationally popular?

24 What type of dessert is cassata?

25 A popular Australian dessert, consisting of meringue topped with cream and fruit, is named after a famous ballet dancer. What is it called?

Dessin 18.

Dessin 19.

Dessin 20.

Dessin 21.

Dessin 22.

Dessin 23.

Dessin 24.

Dessin 25.

1. In cricket, which batsman holds the record for the most first-class runs in a career?

2. Which United States baseball team holds the record for the most wins in a World Series?

3. What is the playing time in basketball?

4. Who is the world's most capped goalkeeper in soccer?

5. What sport would you be watching if a 'chain crew' appeared on the field?

6. What sport would you be watching if a fireman comes on as a relief?

7. In which sport would you compete for the Cowdray Cup?

8. Australians Ray Lindwall and Keith Miller were famous in which team sport?

9. In what sport could you use an Iron Mike in training?

10. Which ice-hockey player was bought by Los Angeles Kings from Edmonton Oilers for $15 million?

11 Where does the umpire-in-chief stand in baseball?

12 Why did the selection of Basil d'Oliveira for the English cricket tour of 1968 cause an international furore?

13 Which famous American team has featured in two films and a cartoon series since being formed in 1927 by Abraham Saperstein? ◀

14 How many innings for each side will there be in a game of baseball?

15 In which team sport was Holland's Johan Cruyff famous?

16 Which great baseball star set 76 batting and pitching records in his 22-year career? ▼

17 Fast pitch and slow pitch are types of the indoor version of baseball. What is it?

18 Who is the only test cricketer to be created a life peer?

19 In which particular sport are penalties awarded to the opposing team for hooking, holding and clipping?

20 How many players does men's lacrosse have on each side?

21 Britain's world famous Lords cricket ground was founded in 1787. The present ground was first opened in 1814, in which area of London can it be found?

22 Pato is a version of which game?

23 What are the most runs scored off one over in first class cricket?

24 The sport of water polo is played by two teams of up to 13 people a side. How many of each team may actually be in the water at one given time?

25 In which sport are Dev, Lillee and Crowe famous?

1 The ancient Egyptians wrote on papyrus. What was it made from?

2 Who was the Queen of the Iceni who fought the Romans and who, according to legend, had knives on the wheels of her chariot?

3 Where was the Hittite empire?

4 Who was the first Emperor of Rome, who came to power in 27BC?

5 Which of the Seven Wonders of the World did Nebuchadnezzar, King of Babylon from 605 to 562 BC, build?

6 The English king Harold was killed in the battle against William the Conqueror. How, according to popular tradition, was he killed?

7 The tomb of 18th dynasty Pharaoh Tutankhamun, containing rich treasure, was discovered in 1922. How old was Tutankhamun when he died? ▼ ▶

8 What was the first Roman name for London?

9 Who was the first Christian missionary?

10 Name the god of the underworld worshipped by the ancient Egyptians?

14 The Roman emperor Caligula created a new consul, Incitatus, in the year 41 AD. Why did this cause consternation?

15 St. Patrick, the patron saint of Ireland, was the Romano-British son of an army officer. How did he first arrive in Ireland?

16 Which Roman general became Cleopatra's lover and ruled Egypt with her?

17 What happened to Julius Caesar on the Ides of March?

18 What was the name given to money demanded by the Vikings from kings in the countries they invaded, as a bribe to leave them and their lands in peace?

19 How many cohorts would actually make up a Roman legion?

20 A spectacular British archaeological find was made in 1939 in Sutton Hoo, Suffolk. What was uncovered?

21 Offa's Dyke was built to divide England from Wales, possibly to mark an agreed border, possibly as part of a defensive system. Where did King Offa rule?

11 In which country was Brian Boru king?

12 Moses led the Hebrew people out of Egypt but died before he could lead them into Canaan. Who was his successor?

13 The Greek philosopher Socrates made many enemies by questioning accepted beliefs and he was eventually tried for corruption of the young and sentenced to death. What was the exact sentence?

22 Plato was a celebrated philosopher. What was his home city?

23 As what did Homer become famous?

24 The Anglo-Saxons wrote with letters they believed to have magical properties. What were they called?

25 Which ancient people did the Romans call barbarians?

1. What is another name for the rowan tree?

2. Which flower is named after the botanist Dr Leonhard Fuchs?

3. From which plant does the pain-killing drug morphine come?

4. What name is given to the Japanese art of growing miniature trees? ▲

5. Which plant is the national emblem of Ireland?

6. Who is said to have worked out the theory of gravity as a result of sitting under an apple tree?

7. What do yew, laburnum seeds and mistletoe berries have in common?

8. Give the popular name for the antirrhinum.

9. What are plants that flower every year called?

10. Which plant takes its name from the Italian phrase for 'beautiful woman'?

11. What name is given to a flowerhead made up of many tiny flowers?

12. Which Swedish naturalist introduced the present-day system of plant classification?

13 By what name is the plant 'digitalis' popularly known?

14 Trees that do not shed their leaves in winter belong to which group?

15 Which salad vegetable has varieties called iceberg and cos?

16 What is the loss of water from the leaves of plants called?

17 How is it possible to tell the age of a tree?

18 Which flower takes its name from the Turkish word for 'turban'?

19 What is the common name for Prunus domestica?

20 Which particular part of the flower is called the anther?

21 What is the difference between dicotyledon and monocotyledon plants?

22 Name the liquid made by a flower to attract insects? ▼

23 In the world classification system for plants, what are aquatic plants containing chlorophyll always called?

24 What is the popular name for the most deadly fungus, the exremely poisonous Amanita phalloides?

25 What is the sacred flower of the Buddhist tradition?

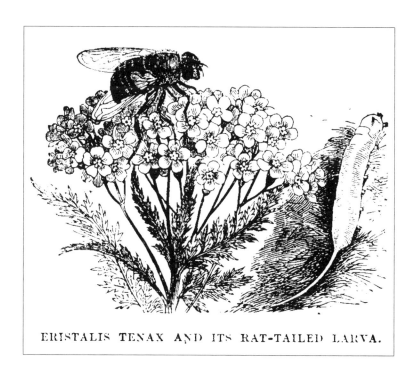

ERISTALIS TENAX AND ITS RAT-TAILED LARVA.

1 Businessman Asil Nadir left Britain after accusations of fraud over the running of his Polly Peck empire. To which country did he flee?

2 Which president of the Philippines was forced to flee the country after the United States withdrew support for him?

3 Live Aid was one of the largest ever fund-raising concerts in 1985. What was it in aid of? ▲ ▶

4 In 1985, Palestinian terrorists hi-jacked an Italian cruise liner in the Mediterranean and murdered a disabled American tourist. Name the ship.

5 Shortly after his inauguration, Ronald Reagan was shot by John Hinckley. Why did Hinckley claim that he attempted assassination?

6 Who led the fundamentalist Islamic regime in Iran at the time of the United States hostage crisis?

7 What was the scene of America's worst nuclear accident, in 1979?

8 Which party did Jimmy Carter represent?

9 Who was known as Stormin' Norman?

10 The Symbionese Liberation Army kidnapped an American heiress, daughter of a millionaire newspaper tycoon in 1974. What was her name?

11 Who was murdered by the IRA at Mullaghmore in Ireland on 27 August, 1979?

12 What post was held by H.R. Haldeman at the time of Watergate?

13 Which militant black American leader was assassinated in 1965?

14 Why did Patricia Cahill and Karen Smith feature in the British headlines in July 1993?

15 Who succeeded Mikhail Gorbachev as Russian leader in 1991?

16 The British government broke off diplomatic relations with which country after the shooting of WPC Fletcher in 1984?

17 How did Provisional IRA member Bobby Sands die in May 1981?

18 Which British newspaper tycoon, his empire deep in debt, was lost overboard from his yacht in November 1991?

19 Which Soviet dissident, husband of Yelena Bonner, was released from internal exile in December 1986?

20 Name the Argentinean cruiser sunk by the British during the Falklands conflict.

21 In December 1989, United States troops invaded Panama and the country's dictator was ousted from power. Name him.

22 The agreement signed between the Israelis and Palestinians in September 1993 gave the Palestinians autonomy in which areas?

23 Of what was John Demjanjuk cleared in 1993?

24 Name the Australian prime minister who discussed severing constitutional ties with Britain with the Queen during a visit to Britain in 1993?

25 Over what incident did the Princess of Wales take legal action in November 1993?

1 In which film did Elvis Presley play the role of a boxer? ▼

2 Which outlaw was killed by Bob Ford?

3 Who was Tsar Nicholas II's youngest daughter?

4 Who won the Pulitzer Prize for his Profiles of Courage?

5 In the Bible, whose parents were Zacharias and Elizabeth?

6 Tariffs and quotas are some of the weapons used in which kind of war?

7 Of which country was Sir Keith Holyoake Prime Minister?

8 From which inn did Chaucer's pilgrims set out in Canterbury Tales?

9 If you had tinnitus, from what would you be suffering?

10 Who was the creator of fictional detective Mike Hammer?

11 In which sport has Stephen Roche achieved success?

12 Which country is the home of feta cheese?

13 Name the 1969 'road' movie starring Dennis Hopper and Peter Fonda as two nonconformist motorcyclists.

14 Larry Hagman is the son of which famous actress? ▲

15 Whose autobiography was entitled Is that it?

16 In which American state is the university of Princeton?

17 What was once called brimstone?

18 In which war were the battles of Bunker Hill and Brandywine Creek fought?

19 Which well-loved cartoon animal made his debut in 1937?

20 What does a protractor measure?

21 What name is given to the person authorized to vote on behalf of someone else?

22 Who said the famous phrase 'An army marches on its stomach'?

23 Iceland and England broke off diplomatic relations in 1976. What particular problem caused the split?

24 Fats Waller was famous as a player of which instrument?

25 Who defined democracy as 'government of the people, by the people, for the people'?

People and Places   Capitals

1. Wellington, New Zealand
2. Western (Wailing) Wall
3. A famous art collection
4. Sri Lanka
5. Kremlin
6. Waikiki
7. Rive Gauche (Left Bank)
8. 99 years
9. Beirut
10. Métro
11. Liechtenstein
12. Berlin
13. Sliema
14. Copenhagen
15. La Paz, Bolivia
16. Paris
17. District of Columbia
18. Beijing (Peking)
19. Lusaka
20. Bangkok
21. Reykjavik, Iceland
22. River Danube
23. A return visit
24. Cairo
25. Brussels

Entertaining Arts   Leading Men

1. Christopher Lee
2. Peter O'Toole
3. On Golden Pond
4. Topol
5. Tony Curtis
6. Charlie Chaplin
7. True Grit
8. Paul Newman
9. Robert Preston
10. Clint Eastwood
11. The Beggar's Opera
12. Dustin Hoffman
13. Robert Mitchum
14. Richard Attenborough
15. The Hunter
16. George C. Scott
17. Orson Welles
18. Claus von Bulow
19. Yul Brynner
20. Noël Coward
21. On the Waterfront and The Godfather
22. Kevin Costner
23. Richard Burton
24. Michael Caine
25. Charlton Heston

Food and Drink   Desserts and Sweets

1. Zabaglione
2. Flambéed in kirsch
3. Bavarois
4. Criss-crossed pastry strips
5. A mixture of fresh or dried fruit in syrup
6. Choux
7. Suet crust
8. As medicine
9. Semolina
10. They were sent to the Anzacs troops, the Australia,
New Zealand Army Corps
11. Pale green
12. The root of the marsh-mallow plant
13. The sugar is caramelized under a high grill
14. Liquorice
15. Ice-cream
16. Chewing gum
17. Currants, peel and sugar
18. Biscuit
19. It is steeped in honey
or sugar syrup
20. Jelly-beans
21. It has several layers of crisp puff pastry, hence 'a thousand leaves'
22. Chantilly cream
23. Black forest cherry cake (Schwarzwälder Kirschtorte)
24. Ice cream
25. Pavlova (named after Anna Pavlova)

Sports and Pastimes   Team Games

1. Jack Hobbs
2. New York Yankees
3. 60 minutes with three intervals
4. Pat Jennings
5. American football
6. Baseball
7. Polo
8. Cricket
9. Baseball
10. Wayne Gretzky
11. Behind the catcher
12. South Africa objected because he was 'coloured'
13. Harlem Globetrotters
14. Nine
15. Soccer
16. Babe Ruth
17. Softball
18. Leery Constantine
19. Ice hockey
20. Ten
21. St. John's Wood
22. Polo
23. 36
24. Seven
25. Cricket

History   Ancient Days

1. Reeds
2. Boudicca (Boadicea)
3. Anatolia, Turkey
4. Augustus
5. Hanging Gardens of Babylon
6. With an arrow through the eye
7. 18
8. Londinium
9. The apostle Paul
10. Osiris
11. Ireland
12. Joshua
13. Death by drinking hemlock
14. Incitatus was a horse
15. He was captured by Irish pirates and sold as a slave
16. Mark Antony
17. He was assassinated
18. Danegeld
19. 10
20. Anglo-Saxon burial ship
21. Mercia
22. Athens
23. Poet and storyteller
24. Runes
25. All those who lived outside the Empire

Natural World   Plants

1. Mountain ash
2. Fuchsia
3. Opium poppy
4. Bonsai
5. Shamrock
6. Isaac Newton
7. They are all poisonous
8. Snapdragon
9. Perennial
10. Belladonna
11. A composite flower
12. Karl Linnaeus
13. Foxglove
14. Evergreens
15. Lettuce
16. Transpiration
17. From the rings within the trunk
18. Tulip
19. Plum
20. The top of the stamen, where the pollen is found in pollen sacs
21. The dicotyledon has
two seed leaves; monocotyledon has only one
22. Nectar
23. Algae
24. Death cap
25. Lotus

Twentieth Century   Headline News

1. North Cyprus
2. Ferdinand Marcos
3. Victims of the Ethiopian famine
4. Achille Lauro
5. To impress actress Jodie Foster with whom he was obsessed
6. Ayatollah Khomeini
7. Three Mile Island
8. Democratic
9. General H. Norman
Schwarzkopf
10. Patty Hearst
11. Earl Mountbatten
12. Presidential Chief of Staff
13. Malcolm X
14. They were released from a prison sentence for drug offences in Thailand
15. Boris Yeltsin
16. Libya
17. He was on hunger strike in prison
18. Robert Maxwell
19. Andrei Sakharov
20. General Belgrano
21. Manuel Noriega
22. Jericho and Gaza Strip
23. Of being the Nazi war criminal, Ivan the Terrible
24. Paul Keating
25. Unauthorized photos of her exercising in a gym

Pot Luck

1. Kid Galahad
2. Jesse James
3. Anastasia
4. John F. Kennedy
5. John the Baptist
6. Trade
7. New Zealand
8. The Tabard at Southwark
9. Ringing or buzzing in the ears
10. Mickey Spillane
11. Cycling
12. Greece
13. Easy Rider
14. Mary Martin
15. Bob Geldof
16. New Jersey
17. Sulphur
18. War of American Independence
19. Bugs Bunny
20. Angles
21. Proxy
22. Napoleon
23. Cod-fishing rights
24. Piano
25. Abraham Lincoln

Quiz

10

1 Woody Allen said, 'It was the most fun I ever had without laughing!' To what was he referring?

2 What was the famous sign on United States President Harry S. Truman's desk?

3 According to film producer Sam Goldwyn, 'a verbal contract is not worth...'. What? ▲

4 Which TV cop would say 'Who loves ya, baby?'

5 'You can fool all of the people some of the time and some of the people all of the time but...'. Complete this quotation from Abraham Lincoln.

6 Which British monarch said 'We are not amused'?

7 Whom did H.G. Wells say was king in 'the country of the blind'?

8 Oscar Wilde said that fox-hunting was the 'unspeakable in pursuit' of what?

9 'Frankly my dear, I don't give a damn'. In which film were these words spoken?

10 Whom did Churchill describe as a 'sheep in sheep's clothing'?

11 Who resigned from the Hollywood Club, saying that he would not want to belong to any club that would accept him as a member?

12 Which music-hall star sang, 'A little of what you fancy does you good'?

13 Which blonde bombshell said 'Keep a diary and one day it will keep you'?

14 British fashion designer Mary Quant said 'A woman is as young as ...'. What?

15 Jean Jacques Rousseau said 'Man was born free and everywhere he is ...'. Complete the quotation.

16 Who sang that 'Mad dogs and Englishmen go out in the midday sun'?

17 Marilyn Monroe, after posing for a revealing photograph, was asked 'Didn't you have anything on?' What was her reply? ▶

18 Which Nazi said in a 1936 broadcast 'Guns will make us powerful – butter will only make us fat'?

19 The saying 'May the force be with you' comes from which film?

20 Maurice Chevalier said 'I prefer old age ...' to what?

21 Which famous Hollywood actress said she had never hated a man enough to give him back his diamonds?

22 Which world leader said in September 1993, 'Enough of blood and tears, enough'?

23 In which film did the main character, played by Bette Davis, say 'Fasten your seatbelts. It's going to be a bumpy night'?

24 Karl Marx said that the workers had nothing to lose but what?

25 Sophie Tucker said the famous lines'I have been poor and I have been rich.' Complete the quotation.

1 What is the subject of a mystery play?

2 Who sold his soul to the devil in a play by Goethe?

3 Who wrote Separate Tables, The Winslow Boy and The Browning Version?

4 In what type of stage production would you find a dame?

5 Who became the first director of Britain's National Theatre?

6 The first big popular success of the 0ff-Broadway musical came with a revival of the Threepenny Opera in 1954. Who wrote it?

7 Who goes mad and commits suicide in Hamlet?

8 What is the name of the space above the proscenium in the theatre, from which the scenery is controlled?

9 What type of plays did the French dramatist Molière write? ▼

10 Who was Joseph Grimaldi?

11 Which Shakespearean play concerns the fortunes of the Montagues and the Capulets?

12 Name the Australian performer who has become famous as Dame Edna Everage?

13 What play holds the record for the longest continuous run in Britain?

14 Name the Irish dramatist who wrote Juno and the Paycock and The Plough and the Stars?

15 Which was Shakespeare's shortest play?

16 In which country is a type of play called kabuki performed?

17 Who were the hero and heroine of the Italian Commedia dell'arte?

18 Oscar Wilde said 'The play was a great success but the audience ...'. Complete the quotation. ▲

19 What is the name of the Mr. Punch's wife in the puppet play?

20 Which early theatre performed its dramas in verse, with the action punctuated by a chorus and with the actors wearing masks?

21 What is the part of the stage that projects into the auditorium called?

22 In which pantomime does the main character 'turn again' with his faithful cat?

23 What happened to London's original Globe Theatre in 1613?

24 Who wrote the music for The Phantom of the Opera?

25 Which of the great writer Shakespeare's plays is the subject of great superstition among actors, so that many will not use its name for fear of disaster?

1. What is the name given to a small field used for rice cultivation?

2. Sugar cane is the largest member of which family?

3. 3. From what is chocolate and cocoa made?

4. What is the other name for vegetables known as legumes?

5. From which substance do bees manufacture honey?

6. The people of which country consume most beef?

7. In which century was margarine invented?

8. Mutton comes from sheep of what age?

9. Geese are bred for their meat and for what else?

10. What type of foodstuff is sorghum, used as a staple diet in Africa and parts of Asia, though rarely in the west?

11. What are Brown Swiss, Finn and Normandy?

12. Which meat was once the staple diet of sailors and early settlers because it could be salted and kept without refrigeration?

13. What is the name for the system of keeping chickens in tiers of cages, with the eggs they lay running down into containers outside the cages?

14 What is a male duck called?

15 In which century was tea drinking introduced into Europe?

16 What are Andalusian, Berkshire and Duroc?

17 When raising beef cattle, what is the name of the system where animals are provided with fodder rather than being allowed to graze?

18 In which country were pigs first used for food?

19 What was normally used as a sweetener before sugar was available?

20 Which country provides about half the coffee consumed in the world?

21 What crop is attacked by the Colorado beetle?

22 Which cereal forms the staple diet of three-quarters of the world's population?

23 Where does maple syrup come from?

24 What are Plymouth Rocks, Barnevelder and Leghorns?

25 The meat veal comes from very young dairy cattle. At what particular age are they usually slaughtered?

1 Which boxer had the most world title fights in his career?

2 Which black American won four gold medals in track and field events in front of Adolf Hitler at the 1936 Berlin Olympics?

3 In golf, who was the first European to win the U.S. Masters?

4 In which ball sport is the U.S. sportsman Magic Johnson famous?

5 Which English woman cricketer has played in the most test matches?

6 Who was the first man to run a mile in under four minutes?

7 Which Portuguese woman has won the Boston Marathon twice and the London Marathon once?

8 Since 1977 the World Snooker Championships have been played at a theatre in northern England. Name it.

9 Which Wimbledon tennis champion was nick-named 'Superbrat'? ▲

10 Paavo Nurmi won nine Olympic medals for distance running in the 1920s and set 29 world records in his career. Which was his home country?

11 The story of which British runners is told in the film Chariots of Fire? ▶

12 By what first name is Frances Morgan Thompson better known?

13 Name the American who won Olympic gold medals in the long jump in 1984, 1988 and 1992?

14 Who did Pete Sampras beat in the 1993 Wimbledon Finals?

15 Which motor racing driver has won most Grand Prix races in his career?

16 Which American athlete is known as 'Flo-Jo'?

17 Who skated to victory to the strains of Ravel's Bolero?

18 What was tennis star Billie Jean King's maiden name?

19 Which East German girl broke the world record for the 400 metres seven times between 1978 and 1985?

20 Mark Todd rode his horse Charisma to victory in the three day event in the Olympics of 1984 and again in 1988. Which country did he represent?

21 Which two West Indian cricketers have been knighted?

22 In which sport are the Cincinnati Reds, Toronto Blue Jays and Los Angeles Dodgers winning teams?

23 Which golfer has most wins in the world's major golf tournaments?

24 Whom did Britain Steve Davis defeat in his very first World Championship snooker final in 1981?

25 In which sport did the Brazilian Pelé achieve fame?

1. Who, in 1895, first fitted pneumatic tyres to a car? ▲

2. In which country did the bullet train – at the time, the fastest train in the world – start running in 1964?

3. What is the distance between the two rails of a railway track called?

4. What, in car production, is CAD?

5. What is a Ro-Ro vessel?

6. In air travel, what do the initials ATC stand for?

7. In which year did the jumbo jet make its maiden flight?

8. What form of transport, mainly made of wood, was invented by Gottlieb Daimler in 1885?

9. It took seven years to build the first railroad from east to west across America and teams of workers started from each end. In which state did they meet? ▶

10. In the 1920s and 1930s, the Orient Express was one of the most glamorous trains in the world. Some carriages have been restored and run to various exotic locations. What is the train now called?

11. In San Francisco tubes run under the Bay on a system called BART. What do the initials stand for?

12. Lagos, in Nigeria, has introduced its own method of traffic control. What happens on Mondays, Wednesdays and Fridays?

13 Who invented the first internal combustion engine to run on petroleum in 1885?

14 What were the Rainhill trials, held in England in 1829?

15 In 1891, the Tsar of Russia ordered the building of a railway between Moscow and Vladivostock and the first train ran in 1901. What was the railway called?

16 What is given the name 'piggy-back transport'?

17 Which new type of passenger ferry appeared in 1959?

18 What make of car featured in Back to the Future?

19 In which year did Concorde, the world's only successful supersonic airliner, first fly?

20 In 1986 Dick Rutan and Jeana Yeager piloted Voyager around the world. What 'first' did they achieve?

21 What is the national civil aircraft mark of the United Kingdom?

22 Where does the new motorway called the Autoput run?

23 Which building is known as the world's largest railway station?

24 The train of the future is the Maglev, which has no wheels but floats above a magnetic track. What does 'Maglev' stand for?

25 Where is the highest railway line in the world to be found?

1 The world's highest waterfall is in Venezuela. What is it called?

2 Which island is famous for its giant tortoises?

3 In Antarctica, an active volcano is covered with snow but still spouts steam. Name it.

4 Where is the world's longest fjord: Iceland, Greenland or Norway?

5 The Grand Canyon, in the United States, is a geologist's paradise. Is the youngest of its rock formations 100 million, 175 million or 225 million years old? ▼

6 Caverns formed in what type of rock have stalactites and stalagmites?

7 What was named after Sir Henry Ayers, Premier of South Australia in 1873?

8 Which is the world's longest river?

9 Rotorua, nicknamed 'sulphur city', has large areas of spectacular geothermal activity – geysers, steam vents and hot springs. In which country is it?

10 What is the most distinctive feature of the Auvergne in France's Massif Central?

11 Which author was inspired by the remote Hunza valley in northern Pakistan to create the idyllic Shangri-La in Lost Horizon?

12 Which animal has become a symbol for the endangered species of the world and is used in the logo of the Worldwide Fund for Nature (formerly World Wildlife Fund)?

13 What is the Perseid shower?

14 Which part of the world is advertised in tourist brochures as 'the land of the midnight sun'?

15 Where is the world's largest coral reef to be found?

16 Which country has the highest navigable lake in the world?

17 Which of the world's trees has the longest lifespan?

18 The largest lizards in the world, growing to nearly 4 metres (12 feet) and able to feed on pigs and deer, are found in Indonesia. What are they called? ▲

19 Which musician was inspired by the cave on the Hebridean island of Staffa to write the overture Fingal's Cave?

20 The deepest of the world's lakes is in south-eastern Siberia. What is it called?

21 The Petrified Forest National Park, where ancient forests have turned into minerals, is in which 'desert' in Arizona in the United States?

22 Bungle Bungle, a wild expanse of striped black and orange beehive-shaped rocks, was proclaimed as a rediscovered 'lost world' in 1982. In which country is it?

23 Conservationists believe that the destruction of the rainforests, resulting in increased carbon dioxide in the atmosphere, is contributing to what harmful effect?

24 Which sacred river has a special place in the Hindu religion because it is believed to be a goddess, commanded to flow down from heaven to give immortal life to those whose ashes are covered by her waters?

25 The beautiful Phang Nga Bay in southern Thailand was the setting for the Bond film The Man with the Golden Gun. Who played the villain Scaramanga, who had a private island here?

1 Henri Landru killed a series of women in France in the early years of the century after advertising in 'lonely hearts' columns. What was his nickname?

2 What was the name of Dr. Crippen's secretary and lover?

3 At which fast food restaurant did James Huberty gun down men, women and children in San Ysidro, United States in 1984?

4 Name the mother convicted and later pardoned in the Australian 'dingo baby' case.

5 Who was the last woman hanged for murder in Britain?

6 Name the pregnant actress, wife of Roman Polanski, who was murdered, along with four others by members of the Charles Manson 'family'?

7 In which city was John F. Kennedy assassinated?

8 Christopher Craig shot a British policeman in 1952 but was too young to face the death penalty. Name his 19-year-old companion, who was hanged.

9 Which English lord disappeared after the killing of his children's nanny and has never been heard of again?

10 I want to Live! was the title of a 1958 film telling the story of the murderess Barbara Graham. Who played Graham?

11 American headmistress Jean Harris shot her lover Dr. Herman Tarnower in 1980. For what diet was the doctor world famous?

12 Marguerite Fahmy shot her Egyptian husband Prince Ali Kemal Fahmy Bey in which luxury hotel in London?

13 How old was ex-Beatle John Lennon when he was shot dead in New York? ▼ ▶

14 Who was Ian Brady's female accomplice in the horrific 'Moors Murders'?

15 Which murderer did Richard Attenborough play in the film 10 Rillington Place?

16 For what was Adolf Eichmann tried and convicted in 1961?

17 Who was the toddler killed in Britain by two 11-year-old boys in 1993?

18 In Cold Blood was an account of the murder of the Clutter family in Kansas, United States. Who was the writer?

19 Albert De Salvo spread panic through an American city as he raped and strangled 13 women over 18 months. By what name is he better known?

20 Who shot Robert Kennedy in 1968?

21 Marcel Petiot was found guilty of murdering 25 people in Paris in 1946; he had pretended to help those who wanted to escape the Nazis, but killed them for their cash. How was he executed?

22 Who was the young black man convicted in 1982 of two murders and suspected of the string of killings of black children in Atlanta, United States?

23 Donald Neilson, who killed three sub-postmasters and heiress Lesley Whittle in northern England in the 1970s, earned what nickname because of the hood he wore to commit his crimes?

24 24. Who was the British MP, shadow Northern Ireland Secretary, killed by a terrorist bomb as he drove from the House of Commons car park in 1979?

25 David Berkowitz, the infamous killer who shot a number of young couples for no apparent reason, taunted the police with strange letters signed by what name?

1. Where is the Dewey classification system used?

2. In what field did Sir Alexander Korda make his name? ▲

3. A tithe was a tax paid to support the clergy. What proportion of income was a tithe?

4. What nationality is the novelist Patrick White?

5. What is the common name for rubella?

6. In which year was the state of Israel created?

7. How old was Rose Kennedy, mother of J.F.K., in July 1993?

8. In which country was Archbishop Makarios President?

9 In the 1992 summer Olympics, three new medal events were added. Two of these were Badminton and Baseball. What was the third?

10 What was Bob Hope's signature tune?

11 Which English Prime Minister once edited The Church Times?

12 Who is the chief god of Scandinavian mythology?

13 For what purpose was the Leaning Tower of Pisa originally built? ▶

14 What was the name of the Mafia patriarch played by Marlon Brando in The Godfather?

15 For what was the Haight-Ashbury area of San Francisco famous in the 1960s?

16 Which Scandinavian country achieved its independence from Sweden in 1905?

17 If you were ailurophobic, what would you fear?

18 After how many years of marriage is a ruby wedding celebrated?

19 Where in London would you find the Whispering Gallery?

20 Which Nobel prize-winning writer shot himself in 1961?

21 In Italy, what is the capital city of Tuscany?

22 Veni, vidi, vici wrote Julius Caesar. What is the translation?

23 Which comedy team included John Cleese, Michael Palin, Graham Chapman and Terry Jones?

24 What would you do with an ocarina?

25 Name the lawyer in Dickens' Tale of Two Cities who finally goes to the guillotine in place of another.

People and Places   Who Said What

1. Sex
2. 'The buck stops here'
3. '... the paper it's written on'
4. Kojak, played by Telly Savalas
5. '... you can't fool all of the people all of the time'
6. Queen Victoria
7. The one-eyed man
8. The uneatable
9. Gone with the Wind
10. Clement Attlee
11. Groucho Marx
12. Marie Lloyd
13. Mae West
14. Her knee
15. '... in chains'
16. Noel Coward
17. 'I had the radio on'
18. Goering
19. Star Wars
20. '... the alternative'
21. Zsa Zsa Gabor
22. Yitzhak Rabin, Premier of Israel
23. All About Eve
24. Their chains
25. 'Rich is better'

Entertaining Arts   Treading the Boards

1. Bible stories or the lives of saints
2. Faust
3. Terence Rattigan
4. Pantomime
5. Peter Hall
6. Bertolt Brecht
7. Ophelia
8. Flies
9. Comedies
10. A clown
11. Romeo and Juliet
12. Barry Humphries
13. The Mousetrap
14. Sean O'Casey
15. The Comedy of Errors
16. Japan
17. Harlequin and Columbine
18. '... was a disaster'
19. Judy
20. Greek theatre
21. Apron
22. Dick Whittington
23. It burned down
24. Andrew Lloyd Webber
25. Macbeth

Food and Drink   Feeding the World

1. Paddy
2. Grass
3. The pods of cacao trees
4. Pulses
5. Nectar
6. United States
7. 19th century
8. Over two years
9. Feathers and down
10. Grain
11. Types of dairy cow
12. Pork
13. Battery
14. Drake
15. 18th
16. Pigs
17. Lot-feeding
18. China
19. Honey
20. Brazil
21. Potato
22. Rice
23. The sap of maple trees
24. Hens
25. Before three months

Sports and Pastimes   The Winners

1. Joe Louis
2. Jesse Owens
3. Seve Ballesteros
4. Basketball
5. Rachael Heyhoe-Flint
6. Roger Bannister
7. Rosa Mota
8. The Crucible Theatre, Sheffield
9. John McEnroe
10. Finland
11. Harold Abrahams and
   Eric Liddell
12. Daley
13. Carl Lewis
14. Jim Courier
15. Alain Prost
16. Florence Griffith-Joyner
17. Jayne Torvill and Christopher Dean
18. Moffitt
19. Marita Koch
20. New Zealand
21. Garfield Sobers and
   Frank Worrell
22. Baseball
23. Jack Nicklaus
24. Doug Mountjoy
25. Soccer

History   Transport

1. Edouard Michelin
2. Japan
3. Gauge
4. Computer-aided design
5. Roll on, roll off
6. Air traffic control
7. 1969
8. Motorbike
9. Utah
10. Venice Simplon Orient Express
11. Bay Area Rapid Transit system
12. Only cars with even numbers on the license plates can use the roads
13. Daimler
14. Locomotive trials
15. Trans-Siberian Railway
16. Container carried by rail
17. Hovercraft
18. De Lorean
19. 1969
20. The first non-stop round-the-world flight without refuelling
21. G
22. From the Italian-Austrian border to the Greek frontier
23. Grand Central, New York
24. Magnetic levitation

Natural World   Nature's Wonders

1. Angel Falls
2. Galapagos
3. Mount Erebus
4. Greenland
5. 225 million
6. Limestone
7. Ayers Rock
8. The Nile
9. New Zealand
10. Chains of extinct volcanoes
11. James Hilton
12. Giant Panda
13. A spectacular display of meteors, which happens every August, burning up as they hit the Earth's atmosphere
14. Scandinavian countries
15. Great Barrier Reef
16. Peru
17. Giant sequoia
18. Komodo dragons
19. Mendelssohn
20. Lake Baikal
21. Painted Desert
22. Australia
23. Global warming: the greenhouse effect
24. The Ganges
25. Christopher Lee

Twentieth Century   Murders Most Foul

1. Bluebeard
2. Ethel le Neve
3. McDonalds
4. Lindy Chamberlain
5. Ruth Ellis
6. Sharon Tate
7. Dallas, Texas
8. Derek Bentley
9. Lord Lucan
10. Susan Hayward
11. The Scarsdale Diet
12. Savoy
13. 40
14. Myra Hindley
15. John Reginald Christie
16. Nazi war crimes
17. James Bulger
18. Truman Capote
19. The Boston Strangler
20. Sirhan Bishara Sirhan
21. Guillotine
22. Wayne Williams
23. The Black Panther
24. Airey Neave
25. Son of Sam

Pot Luck

1. Libraries
2. Films
3. One tenth
4. Australian
5. German measles
6. 1948
7. 103
8. Cyprus
9. Women's judo
10. Thanks for the Memory
11. Edward Heath
12. Odin
13. As the bell-tower of the cathedral
14. Don Vito Corleone
15. Hippies and flower children
16. Norway
17. Cats
18. 40 years
19. St. Paul's Cathedral
20. Ernest Hemingway
21. Florence
22. I came, I saw, I conquered
23. Monty Python
24. Blow it; it is a musical instrument
25. Sydney Carton

Quiz

11

1 What is the highest mountain in Africa?

2 Which mountains form the backbone of South America?

3 Where would you go to look for the Abominable Snowman?

4 Who wrote High Adventure, about a spectacular mountain climb?

5 On which mountain is it said that Noah's Ark came to rest?

6 They were once known as the 'mountains of the moon' and thought to be the source of the Nile. Their name means 'Rainmaker'; what are they?

7 In which country is Tongariro National Park with its three volcanoes, including Mt. Ruapahu?

8 What is the second highest mountain in the world?

9 What was the nationality of the party of climbers who scaled the world's second highest mountain in 1954?

10 The official country retreat of the President of the United States, Camp David, is in which mountains?

11 Which mountain range divides France and Spain?

12 What is Britain's highest mountain?

13 In which country are the Drakensberg mountains?

14 Name the highest mountain in the Alps.

15 Who was with Edmund Hillary when he reached the summit of Everest in 1953? ◄

16 How do the Dolomites get their name?

17 Which mountain, on the island of Honshu, was revered by the Japanese for centuries as a sacred mountain? ▲

18 Name the active volcano that stands above the Bay of Naples.

19 The highest mountain in North America is in Alaska. What is it called?

20 Which ancient civilization was nurtured in the Andes?

21 The world's third highest mountain is Kanchenjunga. What nationality were the climbers who first reached the mountain's summit in 1955?

22 Which mountains stretch from northern Canada to the southern United States?

23 How does Cotopaxi in the Andes of Ecuador earn its place in the record books?

24 How did climbers George Leigh Mallory and Andrew Irving find a place in mountaineering history?

25 Name the mountain named in the Bible on which Moses was given the Ten Commandments.

1. Who plays the incompetent proprietor of Fawlty Towers?

2. Golden Girls was a great success; which of the 'girls' is missing from the sequel, Golden Palace?

3. How were Gene Wilder and Richard Pryor dressed when they were arrested in the film Stir Crazy?

4. Who lived at Railway Cuttings, East Cheam?

5. Which comedienne, who starred with Lenny Henry in Three of a Kind, went to the United States in 1987 where, by the end of her first season, her show was nominated for five Emmy awards?

6. Who wrote the screenplay for Barefoot in the Park, based on his Broadway success?

7. I Love Lucy was the first American sit-com seen in Britain. Who was the star?

8. Which American comedian based much of his act on his meanness and incompetent violin playing?

9. Who does Paul Eddington play in Yes Minister?

10. Which comedian is the husband of Dawn French?

11. A Clown Too Many is the autobiography of which British comedian who died in 1993?

12. In which city is the bar in Cheers situated?

13. Who played the incompetent medium Madame Arcati in the 1954 film of Blithe Spirit?

14. In which film did Tony Curtis and Jack Lemmon dress in drag and join an all-girls band?

15. George Burns starred in a TV show with his wife for eight seasons before she retired. What was her name? ▶

16. In A Fish Called Wanda, what is the profession of the character played by John Cleese?

17. With whom did Penelope Keith star in To the Manor Born and Executive Stress?

18. Which sergeant was played by Phil Silvers?

19. What was John Inman's catchphrase as Mr. Humphries in Are You Being Served?

20. Which comedy quartet was made up of Spike Milligan, Harry Secombe, Peter Sellers and Michael Bentine?

21. Glenda Jackson won an Oscar for best actress when she starred opposite George Segal in a comedy in 1973. What was the film?

22. Who played the 'odd couple' in the 1968 film?

23. Which English comedian, famous for the bawdy humour of his shows, in which he created characters like Fred Skuttle and chased scantily-clad girls, had a great success on American TV?

24. Name the sit-com set in occupied France with stories involving resistance workers and stupid German officers.

25. Which actor, the first black actor to share equal billing with a white actor on American TV in I Spy, went on to star in a sit-com about a middle-class black family, and became the highest-paid sitcom star?

6 Oysters are an expensive delicacy. What does it mean if they are 'shucked'? ◀ ▶

7 Where would you expect to eat paella?

8 If you ordered lassi as a drink with an Indian meal, it could be flavoured with salt and pepper, sugar or fruit. What is it made from?

9 What is the main ingredient of guacamole?

10 What type of food is gazpacho?

11 Which bread, sliced very thinly and crisped in the oven, is named after a famous opera singer?

12 What salad is made from chopped apple, celery, walnuts and creamy mayonnaise dressing?

13 What salad is made from diced cucumber, tomatoes, feta cheese and black olives, dressed with olive oil and lemon juice?

14 What type of food is pepperoni?

15 In a Japanese restaurant, diners might order a dish of thinly sliced beef and raw vegetables, which would be stir-fried at the table. What is it called?

16 At what stage of a meal would you eat rillette?

17 A vacherin may be filled with whipped cream or ice-cream and fruit. From what is the case made?

18 What type of food is Bombay duck?

19 On an American menu, what are home fries?

1 What is the Italian name for squid?

2 A 'smoothie' is a popular drink in Australia. Its ingredients are blended with ice until frothy; what are they?

3 Where was chop suey invented?

4 What food has a name that literally means 'on a skewer'?

5 Blinis are small, yeasted pancakes. With what are they traditionally served ?

20 If you were looking at an American menu and wanted to order fried potatoes mashed in a pan and crisped on both sides, what would they be called?

21 What is the Swedish name for hot or cold dishes served as a buffet?

22 If you ordered gratin dauphinois, what would you expect to be served?

23 What is the name given to small cubes of bread, fried or toasted, that can be sprinkled on soups or salads?

24 What name is given to the type of coffee where steam is forced through very finely ground coffee, making a very strong brew?

25 Which type of meat usually goes into frankfurters?

1 Which side of a boat is port?

2 In what sport might you 'catch a crab'?

3 What is the name given to decompression sickness caused by ascending too fast from a deep dive?

4 Who was the first man to swim the English Channel in 1875?

5 In water polo, the game is divided into four quarters. How long is each quarter?

6 There are two main types of canoe: the kayak and the Canadian canoe. What is the difference between the paddles?

7 What do the letters SCUBA stand for?

8 What is a warp?

9 To what do the following rules apply: reach-throw-wade-row-swim/tow?

10 Roland Matthes,was probably one of the greatest ever backstrokers.He was Olympic champion in 1968 and 1972. Which country did this great swimmer represent?

11 Synchronized swimming is one of the newest Olympic sports. In the 1930s, 'water ballet' was a novelty in films. Which star was famous in this discipline?

12 A team in canoe polo consists of how many people?

13 What type of emergency drill is known as buddy breathing?

14 What is the name given to the short tube with a mouthpiece that enables a diver to breathe just below the surface of the water?

15 In sailing, what is turning the boat around through the wind called? ◀

16 Where does the Whitbread Round the World Race, organized by the Royal Naval Sailing Association, start and finish?

17 What are figure-of-eight, sheet bend, bowline and buntline hitch?

18 There are two types of diving competition. One is the highboard; what is the other?

19 When canoeing on rivers and canals, you may sometimes have to negotiate obstacles by portage. What is this?

20 In swimming, a 'pull buoy' is a shaped float held between the legs when practising what?

21 In sailing what is an MOB?

22 The Single-handed Transatlantic Race begins at Plymouth, England. Where does it finish?

23 In water-skiing, what are a cow-catcher and a side-curtain? ▼

24 What is a wake? '

25 Which famous swimmer was suspended for 10 years by the Australian authorities for misbehaviour at the 1964 Olympics, when she led a midnight raid to steal a souvenir flag from the Emperor's palace in Tokyo?

1. Which European explorer discovered the Hawaiian islands?

2. Who beat Captain Robert Scott in the 'race' to the South Pole in 1911-12?

3. Mary Kingsley was one of the first women explorers. Where did she travel?

4. Which French naval officer and underwater explorer invented the aqualung?

5. What nationality was explorer Ferdinand Magellan?

6. Against which disease did Edward Jenner discover a vaccine?

7. Who introduced potatoes and tobacco to England after his voyage of exploration?

8. What was given the name the 'New World'?

9. When Abel Tasman discovered Tasmania, what did he call it?

10. Which United States President became an explorer at age 53 to trace the course of the South American Duvido River, now named after him?

11. Prince Henry of Portugal earned what nickname because he involved himself with so many voyages of exploration?

12. In 1947, Norwegian anthropologist Thor Heyerdahl crossed the Pacific on a raft. What was it called?

13. What name was given to the Spanish conquerors of large parts of south and central America in the 16th century?

14 Which explorer travelled in a ship called the Santa Maria?

15 David Livingstone disappeared while exploring Africa in the 1860s and Henry Stanley led an expedition to find him. What was Stanley's profession? ▼

16 What was crossed on foot for the first time in 1968-9?

17 Who led the expedition that set sail in five ships: the Pelican, the Marigold, the Elizabeth, the Swan and the Christopher?

18 In 1856 two Englishmen, Richard Burton and John Speke, set out through the African continent to find the source of which river?

19 Which part of the world was once known as the 'Dark Continent'?

20 What action did Lawrence Oates take in 1912, believing that he was holding up the exploration team?

21 Bartolomeu Dias called it the 'Cape of Storms'. What is it called now?

22 What was the name of Yuri Gagarin's spaceship in 1961?

23 In which land did Charles Doughty, T.E. Lawrence and Bertram Thomas travel and explore?

24 What nationality was Abel Tasman?

25 Terra Australia Incognita was the name given to the vast continent supposed, until the 18th century, to exist in the southern hemisphere. What does the name mean?

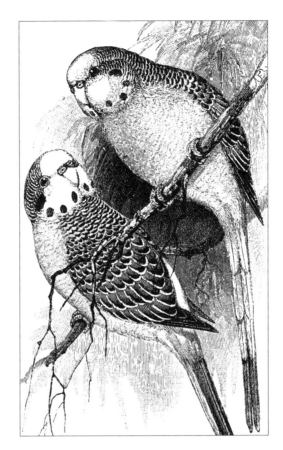

1. Budgerigars of all sorts of colours have been developed by breeders. What colour are they in the wild? ▲

2. What is the other name for a cavy?

3. Which cat has no tail?

4. What dog was once sacred in China?

5. Which breed of dog is the favourite of Queen Elizabeth II?

6. What would live in an apiary?

7. What is the family name of doves and pigeons?

8. From which country does the Korat cat come?

9. For what does the Bloodhound have a special reputation?

10. How many sets of teeth does a dog have in its lifetime?

11 What is the difference between the diet of the tortoise and the terrapin?

12 What type of animals are Cornish Rex and Devon Rex?

13 In which country did poodles originate?

14 Guinea pigs whose coats have two or more colours in a pattern are called 'Marked'. What are those with a single colour called? ▼

15 What is the world's smallest breed of dog?

16 What type of animal are Pinto, Haflinger and Waler?

17 To which bird family does the canary belong?

18 What is unusual about the Basenji dog?

19 Which pets can be Peruvian, Abyssinian or Himalayan?

20 What is distinctive about the coat of a piebald pony?

21 The Maine Coon cat gets part of its name from its native state of Maine, How does it get the second part?

22 Which country is the homeland of the Lhaso Apso dog?

23 What type of creature would lhave an aviary as a home?

24 Which particular domestic animal might be Netherland Dwarfs or New Zealand Whites?

25 Which well-loved breed of dog is known for its stalwart rescue work in the mountains of Europe?

5 Why was the night when Jewish businesses and synagogues were attacked in November 1938 called Kristallnacht?

6 What was the Anschluss, which took place in March 1938?

7 What happened on 1 September, 1939 to precipitate the declaration of war by Britain and France?

8 The Maginot line was a defensive system constructed to protect the French border. How did it get its name?

9 Against which country did Hitler launch 'Operation Barbarossa'?

10 Who was the Desert Fox?

11 What mark did Jews under German rule have to wear on their clothing?

12 American conscripts called themselves GIs. What did the initials stand for?

13 Name the commander of the French armies in World War I who was appointed head of government after Hitler's invasion and was tried as a collaborator at the end of the war.

14 'Let nobody say it cannot be done. It must be done and we are prepared to do it.' Who said this about the 'victory programme' of his country?

15 In 1941 the Japanese attacked the American fleet in Pearl Harbor. Where is Pearl Harbor?

16 In 1943, the Red Army began to drive the Germans from Soviet territory. When they liberated Kiev, what horror did they find at Babi Yar?

17 What was remarkable about Japanese kamikaze pilots?

1 What year did Adolf Hitler rise to power in Germany?

2 What was the name of the Italian dictator who had been in power since 1922?

3 Which treaty had concluded peace after World War I in 1919?

4 What was the name of the political police in Nazi Germany?

18 The codename 'Operation Overlord' was given to which military operation in 1944?

19 Where did Churchill and Roosevelt meet Stalin for a major conference in February 1945?

20 The first meeting of the United Nations Organization was scheduled for 25 April, 1945. What organization did it replace?

21 Which German city suffered the worst bombing of the war in February 1945?

22 The first atom bomb was dropped on Hiroshima. On which city was the second dropped? ◀

23 What trials began in November 1945 to bring war criminals to justice?

24 Which emperor ruled Japan at the time of the war?

25 Name the Jewish girl who kept a famous diary while in hiding from the Nazis in Amsterdam. ▼

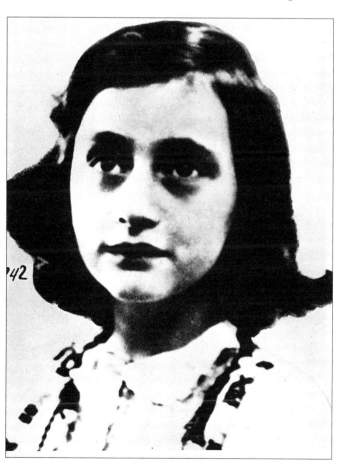

1. Which Commonwealth country celebrated its bicentennial in 1988?

2. What drink is made from vodka and tomato juice?

3. Who is Julie Andrews' director husband? ▲

4. How many points are awarded to the winning driver of a Formula I Grand Prix race?

5. Which zodiac sign is represented by the crab?

6. Which set of sporting rules are named after a 19th–century nobleman?

7. What film included the song Wandering Star?

8. By what name was the fictional Lord Greystoke better known?

9. What was the earliest type of antibiotic drug that was introduced in the 1940s?

10. Who was the Englishman who was saved from death by the Indian girl Pocahontas? ▶

11. Which North African city has a name meaning 'white house' in Spanish?

12. In the Bible, who buried Jesus in his own tomb?

13 Colonel Tom Parker was manager for which famous singer?

14 Under what name is the writer David Cornwell better known?

15 Which type of acid is usually found in car batteries?

16 What does 'C' stand for in film star George C. Scott's name?

17 To which country do the Molucca islands belong?

18 Which male singing voice comes below tenor?

19 In Paris, where is the Tomb of the Unknown Soldier?

20 Who is the world famous film star mother of Jason Gould?

21 What would you do with the Eastern device called a 'hookah'?

22 What type of paintings did artists of the Norwich school produce?

23 In 1943, a group of generals plotted to kill their leader with a bomb. Who was he?

24 Which ancient tribe of invaders gave the country of England and the English people their name?

25 The sea parrot is more usually known by another name. What is it?

People and Places Mountains and Climbers

1. Mt. Kilimanjaro
2. Andes
3. The Himalayas
4. Sir Edmund Hillary
5. Mt. Ararat
6. Ruwenzori
7. New Zealand
8. K2
9. Italian
10. Appalachians
11. Pyrenees
12. Ben Nevis
13. South Africa
14. Mont Blanc
15. Sherpa Tenzing Norgay
16. From the rock of which they are composed
17. Mt. Fuji
18. Vesuvius
19. Mt. McKinley
20. Incas
21. British
22. Rocky Mountains
23. The highest active volcano
24. They disappeared during an Everest climb in 1924; some people think they reached the summit
25. Mt. Sinai

Entertaining Arts A Good Laugh

1. John Cleese
2. Dorothy, played by Bea Arthur
3. As chickens
4. Tony Hancock
5. Tracy Ullman
6. Neil Simon
7. Lucille Ball
8. Jack Benny
9. Jim Hacker
10. Lenny Henry
11. Les Dawson
12. Boston
13. Margaret Rutherford
14. Some Like it Hot
15. Gracie Allen
16. Barrister
17. Peter Bowles
18. Bilko
19. 'I'm free'
20. The Goons
21. A Touch of Class
22. Walter Matthau and Jack Lemmon
23. Benny Hill
24. 'Allo 'Allo
25. Bill Cosby

Food and Drink A la Carte

1. Calamari
2. Milk, yogurt, fruit and honey
3. Chinatown, San Francisco
4. Kebab
5. Sour cream and caviar
6. Opened
7. Spain or a Spanish restaurant
8. Yogurt and ice water
9. Avocado pears
10. Cold soup
11. Melba toast
12. Waldorf salad
13. Greek salad
14. Spicy sausage
15. Sukiyaki
16. As a first course
17. Meringue
18. Fish
19. Sliced or cubed potatoes fried in bacon fat
20. Hash browns
21. Smorgasbord
22. Potatoes topped with cheese
23. Croûtons
24. Espresso
25. Pork

Sports and Pastimes On the Water

1. The left side
2. Rowing
3. The bends
4. Captain Matthew Webb
5. Seven minutes actual playing time
6. The kayak paddle has a blade at each end; the Canadian canoe paddle has one blade
7. Self-contained under water breathing apparatus
8. A rope used to secure a boat
9. Life-saving
10. East Germany
11. Esther Williams
12. Five
13. Two or more divers share an aqualung
14. Snorkel
15. Tacking
16. Portsmouth, England
17. Nautical knots
18. Springboard
19. Carrying the canoe round the obstacle
20. Arm action
21. Man overboard
22. Newport, Rhode Island
23. A safety arrangement on the side of a jump
24. The pair of waves left by the boat
25. Dawn Fraser

History Exploration and Discovery

1. James Cook
2. Roald Amundsen
3. West Africa
4. Jacques Cousteau
5. Portuguese
6. Smallpox
7. Sir Walter Raleigh
8. The newly discovered American continent
9. Van Diemen's Land
10. Theodore Roosevelt
11. Henry the Navigator
12. Kon-Tiki
13. Conquistadors
14. Christopher Columbus
15. Journalist
16. North Pole
17. Sir Francis Drake
18. The Nile
19. Africa
20. Walked out into a blizzard and disappeared
21. Cape of Good Hope
22. Vostok I
23. Arabia
24. Dutch
25. Unknown southern land

Natural World Pets

1. Green
2. Guinea pig
3. Manx
4. Pekingese
5. Corgis
6. Bees
7. Columbidae
8. Thailand
9. Tracking
10. Two
11. The tortoise is vegetarian, the terrapin is carnivorous
12. Cats
13. France
14. Selfs
15. Chihuahua
16. Horses
17. Finch
18. It does not bark
19. Guinea pigs
20. Large, definite and irregular patches of black and white
21. Its coat resembles that of a racoon
22. Tibet
23. Birds
24. Rabbits
25. St. Bernard

Twentieth Century World War II

1. 1933
2. Benito Mussolini
3. Treaty of Versailles
4. Gestapo
5. Because of the glass strewn across the streets; it means 'night of glass'
6. The annexation of Austria by Germany
7. Invasion of Poland
8. Maginot was the minister of war who had it built
9. Russia
10. Field Marshall Rommel
11. Yellow star
12. Government Issue
13. Henri Pétain
14. President Roosevelt
15. Oahu, in the Hawaiian islands
16. Mass grave
17. They were suicide pilots, who died while deliberately crashing their planes into enemy ships
18. Allied landings in Normandy
19. Yalta in the Crimea
20. League of Nations
21. Dresden
22. Nagasaki
23. Nuremberg trials
24. Hirohito
25. Anne Frank

Pot Luck

1. Australia
2. Bloody Mary
3. Blake Edwards
4. 10
5. Cancer
6. Queensbury rules
7. Paint Your Wagon
8. Tarzan
9. Penicillin
10. Captain John Smith
11. Casablanca
12. Joseph of Arimathea
13. Elvis Presley
14. John le Carré
15. Sulphuric acid
16. Campbell
17. Indonesia
18. Baritone
19. Arc de Triomphe
20. Barbra Streisand
21. Smoke it
22. Landscapes
23. Adolf Hitler
24. Angles
25. Puffin

Quiz

12

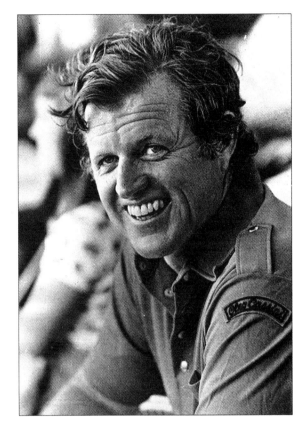

1. What was the name of William Wordsworth's sister.

2. What did Anne Sullivan teach Helen Keller to do?

3. In 1785 George IV of Britain married a Catholic widow, although the marriage was declared illegal by Parliament. What was her name?

4. What feat did Alcock and Brown accomplish in 1919?

5. Who was Ronald Reagan's first wife?

6. How were singers Karen and Richard Carpenter related?

7. Which loyal Highlander helped Prince Charles Edward Stuart to escape to France after the defeat at Culloden?

8. What was the name of Cesare Borgia's influential sister?

9. Which two leaders shared the Nobel Peace Prize in 1993?

10. Whom did both Debbie Reynolds and Elizabeth Taylor marry?

11 Richard III is suspected of having had the 'Princes in the Tower' murdered. What were the boys' names?

12 Which couple, working in France, pioneered research in radioactivity?

13 Sir Ranulph Fiennes set out on the first unassisted crossing of the Antarctic in 1992. Who was with him on this venture?

14 Torvill and Dean became famous as ice dancers. What was Christopher Dean's former profession?

15 Who led the mutiny against Captain Bligh of the Bounty?

16 Stephen, King of England from 1135 to 1154, usurped the crown that belonged to the daughter of Henry I. What was her name?

17 Clark Gable was married to an actress, who died in 1942. Who was she? ▶

18 Who was Shirley Williams' famous mother?

19 Which Russian dancer formed a famous partnership with Margot Fonteyn?

20 In what field did British husband and wife Sidney and Beatrice Webb make their name as pioneers in the last century?

21 Ellen Terry was most famous for her performance in plays by Shakespeare, when she played opposite which actor?

22 Who was Art Garfunkel's singing partner?

23 William III and Mary II were joint rulers of Britain. What relation were they?

24 What was the name of Senator Edward Kennedy's wife? ◀

25 Which tennis champion married John Lloyd?

5 What is Lovejoy's profession?

6 Lee Majors was the Six Million Dollar Man. Who was his female counterpart in Bionic Woman?

7 Which beautiful Bond girl is now a medicine woman?

8 In which series did Christopher Timothy star as a veterinary surgeon? ◀

9 Name the fiery pensioner played by Stephanie Cole in Waiting for God.

10 Who talks for Lamb Chop?

11 Two of the three original stars in Charlie's Angels were Kate Jackson and Jaclyn Smith. Who was the third?

12 Which television series began with a partially naked man playing an organ?

13 Which actress achieved success as Jane Tennison in Prime Suspect but was rejected for the film version?

14 Which actress plays head nurse Hot Lips in M*A*S*H?

15 Name the Cartwright ranch in Bonanza.

16 Which series was based on the real-life adventures of G-man Eliot Ness in prohibition Chicago?

17 In Open All Hours, Ronnie Barker plays a shopkeeper and David Jason also stars. What relation are the two characters?

1 Who plays Lieutenant Columbo in the TV series?

2 The American version of Till Death Us Do Part starred Carroll O'Connor as Archie Bunker. What was it called?

3 What is television's equivalent of the Oscar?

4 Which 1990s series coined the saying 'Who killed Laura Palmer'?

18 The Jewel in the Crown was set in the last days of the British Raj in India. It was based on four novels by Paul Scott. By what name are they known?

19 Who played the green monster in The Incredible Hulk? ▼

20 What was the first name of Grandpa Walton?

21 Which black woman hosts the No. 1 chat show in America, also shown on Britain's Channel 4?

22 Name the English actress who stars with Roy Scheider and Jonathan Brandis in Sea Quest.

23 Which American actor became famous as Lou Grant?

24 In which year was Coronation Street first televised in the United Kingdom?

25 In American soap opera Dallas, who was JR's alchoholic wife?

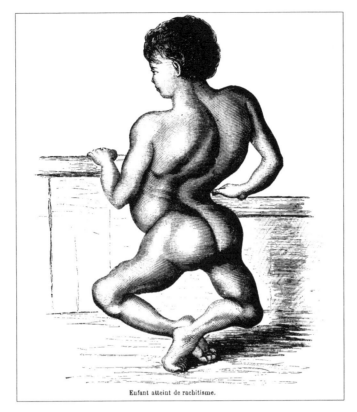

Enfant atteint de rachitisme.

1 In what foodstuff is gluten found?

2 Which vitamin do children with rickets lack? ▲

3 In 1897 a Swiss doctor invented a breakfast food which was a mixture of grains, fruit and nuts. What is it called?

4 TVP is a meat substitute. What do the initials stand for?

5 Babies are born with quite soft bones. What do we give them to provide calcium to harden the bones?

6 What is the name of the mild-flavoured bean curd which looks rather like white blancmange?

7 In which foods is vitamin C mainly found?

8 Why do we pasteurize milk? ▶

9 What are the names of the substances that make up proteins?

10 What name is given to a diet that cuts out all food known to cause allergic reaction or sensitivity?

11 Carrots supply carotene from which the body can make which vitamin?

12 What type of food is Quark?

13 The 'Zen' diet is based on foods divided into two basic groups, Yin and Yang, representing negative and positive elements. What is the other name for this diet?

14 Scurvy is caused by the lack of which vitamin to the body?

15 What is the name given to the eating disorder leading to dramatic weight loss?

16 Vegemite, especially popular in Australia, is one of the richest known sources of B complex vitamins. What is it?

17 Carob is used as a health-conscious substitute for what?

18 The additive tartrazine has been linked with hyperactivity in children. What is it?

19 Liver is high in which vitamin?

20 Which disease results from iron deficiency?

21 Cirrhosis of the liver is linked with what?

22 The 'Chinese Restaurant Syndrome' is the name given to dizziness and headaches caused by eating a lot of food with what additive?

23 Vegans are at risk of a shortage of which vitamin?

24 What enables the body to make vitamin D?

25 In healthy eating, what do the initials RDI stand for?

4 What was the Stumpjumper?

5 In photography, what is the name given to swinging the camera to follow a fast-moving subject so that the picture will be sharp?

6 In a game of chess, what are the limitations on the king's moves?

7 In the sport of skateboarding, what is the 'kick-tail'? ◀

8 What very simple game entails flicking plastic discs into a cup by pressing them sharply with other discs?

9 What is a 'coarse' fish?

10 If a stamp bears the words Deutsche Bundespost, from what country does it come?

11 What does to 'spook' a fish in fly fishing mean? ▶

12 In golf, what is the traditional name for the No. 10 iron?

13 What fantasy game is known as D and D?

14 In bike-riding, what is a 'wheelie'?

15 Where would you play a game called Aunt Sally?

16 On a tent, what name is given to the extra layer of fabric over it, held away so that there is a gap between the two layers?

17 In mountain biking, what is often fixed to the pedals to help when climbing?

1 In photography, what does SLR mean?

2 How many squares are there along one side of a Scrabble board?

3 What does a deltiologist collect?

18 Which game has a name that means 'I play' in Latin?

19 What does a phillumenist collect?

20 What are the north, south, east and west points on a compass called?

21 Omar Sharif is a player of international standard in which games?

22 By what name is toxophily usually known?

23 In what game should you not knock down the skittles?

24 If a postage stamp bears the name Suomi, to which country does it belong?

25 What is the housing used for racing pigeons called?

1. What is the name given to the area of the Atlantic ocean where, since 1945, a number of ships and planes have disappeared without trace?

2. Which cloth, believed by some to be Christ's winding sheet, has been housed in an Italian Cathedral since the 16th century?

3. For what powers did Uri Geller become famous in the 1970s? ▲

4. What do the initials UFO stand for?

5. In the Christian tradition, what are stigmata?

6. What is formed in space when a huge star collapses inwards?

7. Some people believe that stone circles have special powers and are linked by lines of force carrying powerful psychic energy. What are they called?

8. Who might make a wax image of an enemy and stick pins in it?

9. For what did the ship the Marie Celeste become famous in 1872?

10. What name is given to the strange cases where a person bursts into flames for no apparent reason and is incinerated in a matter of minutes?

11. In the legend of The Flying Dutchman, a Dutch sea captain was condemned by God to sail the seas forever with a phantom crew. What was his crime?

12 A mysterious ape-man, similar to the Abominable Snowman, is sometimes sighted in North America. What is it called?

13 What name is given to the legendary creature who is half woman, half fish?

14 Nostradamus is the most famous prophet and forecaster of the future of all time. What was his home country? ▶

15 How were the white horses on the hillsides of Uffington, Pewsey and Cherhill in England made?

16 The Fox sisters of New York State became famous in the last century for their apparent ability to contact the spirit world, though they later confessed to fraud. What is the worldwide movement that started from their supposedly supernatural demonstrations?

17 Name the noisy spirit that causes loud disturbances, throwing things about, banging doors and so on.

18 Hampton Court Palace in England is supposedly haunted by three of Henry VIII's wives. Two of them are Catherine Howard and Jane Seymour. Who is the third?

19 What was the ideal kingdom described by Plato that was supposed to have vanished beneath the sea?

20 What name is given to the phenomenon by which a person or object rises into the air with no means of support?

21 What would you find at Carnac in Brittany, and in Britain at Avebury in Wiltshire and in 'Long Meg and her Daughters' in Cumbria?

22 Reports of vampires were widespread in Europe in the 18th century. According to tradition how must vampires be killed?

23 Several religious legends are associated with Glastonbury in southern England, one of them being that Joseph of Arimathea came here after the death of Christ. Which holy relic did he bring?

24 Which famous American clairvoyant from Washington predicted the deaths of both John and Robert Kennedy?

25 With which island is voodoo particularly associated?

1 Which is the heaviest insect?

2 Where do locusts lay their eggs?

3 What is the job of the soldier ant?

4 Give the other name for the shell of the tortoise or turtle.

5 Where is the rattlesnake's 'rattle'?

6 Why do glow-worms glow in the dark?

7 Bees store food and raise young in hexagonal cells made from what?

8 The earthworm has several pairs of tiny bristles called chaetae on its body. What are they used for?

9 How do a python and a boa kill their prey?

10 The body of an insect is divided into how many sections?

11 Where do dragonflies spend their early life?

12 The loud ticking sound produced by the death watch beetle as it knocks against timbers to attract a mate was once thought to herald what unhappy event?

13 What is an invertebrate?

14 Into what does the butterfly egg hatch?

15 What do the North American Gila monster and the Mexican beaded lizard have in common?

16 Where does the silk moth lay its eggs?

17 To which order do butterflies and moths belong? ◀

18 How does the stag beetle get its name?

19 There are three types of bee in a hive. What are they?

20 How do ants recognize one another?

21 Which are the largest living reptiles and the closest relatives of the dinosaurs?

22 The name of the 'atlas' moth, the largest moth, reflects its size. What is the smallest called?

23 What happens to the garden snail in winter?

24 What name is given to the change insects undergo as they change from larvae to adults?

25 When a snake has its tongue out, what is it likely to be doing? ▼

1 The daily newspaper of the Communist party was called Pravda. What does pravda mean?

2 In 1968 Soviet tanks invaded Czechoslovakia to crush the government's reforming regime. Who was the Czech leader?

3 In which year did the Berlin Wall come down? ▲

4 In which year was the Soviet Union officially dissolved?

5 Eleven of the 15 former Soviet republics formed an alliance known as the CIS. What do the initials stand for?

6 What is the main religion of Lithuania?

7 Which Soviet leader replaced Nikita Krushchev as the first secretary of the Communist party in 1964?

8 What was a gulag?

9 In which decade was the Cultural Revolution in China launched?

10 What is the given name of Mikhail Gorbachev's wife? ▶

11 In which year was the Russian revolution?

12 What is the capital of Latvia?

13 What was formed by ordinary people on 23 August, 1989 to mark the 50th anniversary of the Nazi-Soviet pact, which passed control of the Baltic States to the Soviets?

14 Which two republics dispute the rulership of Nagorno-Karabakh?

15 What is the Russian national drink?

16 Which American President made a historic tour of China in 1972, after the country had been ostracized by the West for some years?

17 What was the name of the most famous checkpoint between East and West Berlin?

18 Gorbachev was very popular abroad; why did he become so unpopular at home?

19 In 1987 Mathias Rust, from West Germany, arrived in Moscow and several military leaders were sacked. How did he arrive?

20 After the break-up of the U.S.S.R. the largest of the republics is the Russian Republic. What is the second largest?

21 By what initials were the Soviet secret police most recently known?

22 Of which republic did Eduard Shevardnadze become acting head in 1992?

23 Which high flying Soviet politician was closely associated with Krushchev, and made several foreign visits with him; then in 1957 was involved in an unsuccessful coup against Krushchev and lost power?

24 Part of the West's defences against the Eastern bloc was the stationing of nuclear missiles on European soil. What type of missiles were sited at Greenham Common in England?

25 Which Polish politician was awarded the Nobel Peace Prize in 1983?

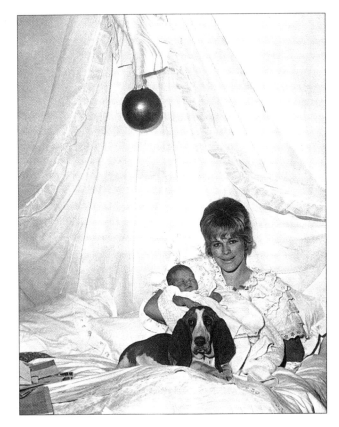

1. Which nocturnal bird known world-wide is the symbol of wisdom?

2. Which disease is the BCG vaccine used to combat?

3. Which famous playwright is the husband of historian Lady Antonia Fraser? ▲

4. Who performed the Dance of the Seven Veils?

5. In a rowing eight, what is the oarsman who sits nearest to the bow called?

6. Who was the Greek goddess of love, known to the Romans as Venus?

7. What medal, founded by George Washington, is awarded to American service personnel wounded in the course of duty?

8. Which hormone contributes to the development of male characteristics?

9. The Castle of Mey is the private residence of which member of the British royal family?

10. How did Princess Grace of Monaco die? ▶

11 What is a group of eight musicians called?

12 The British TV system uses 625 lines. How many does the American system use?

13 What would you do with a 'wandering sailor'?

14 In the financial world, what do the initials MLR stand for?

15 'Blood and Fire' is the motto of which organization?

16 The United Nations flag shows a map of the world. What is on either side of the map?

17 What popular Japanese meal is known as the 'friendship dish'?

18 In the television series, what was the name of Perry Mason's secretary?

19 Dachshunds were originally bred for hunting what?

20 What type of trees grew in the Garden of Gethsemane in Jerusalem?

21 Who played Private Benjamin?

22 Which film actress visited Hanoi to demonstrate her opposition to the Vietnam war?

23 At the summer Olympic Games, athletes from which country always lead the procession of competitors?

24 What do the initials UNESCO stand for?

25 When John F. Kennedy was assassinated, the Governor of Texas was seriously wounded. What was his name?

People and Places   Couples

1. Dorothy
2. Communicate
3. Maria Fitzherbert
4. They flew non-stop across the Atlantic
5. Jane Wyman
6. Brother and sister
7. Flora Macdonald
8. Lucrezia
9. Nelson Mandela and F.W. de Klerk
10. Eddie Fisher
11. Edward and Richard
12. Pierre and Marie Curie
13. Dr Michael Stroud
14. Policeman
15. Fletcher Christian
16. Matilda
17. Carole Lombard
18. Vera Brittain
19. Rudolf Nureyev
20. Socialist politics
21. Henry Irving
22. Paul Simon
23. Cousins and husband and wife
24. Joan
25. Chris Evert

History   Mysteries

1. Bermuda Triangle
2. Turin Shroud
3. Metal-bending
4. Unidentified Flying Object
5. Bleeding from the sites of wounds suffered by Christ on the cross
6. A black hole
7. Ley lines
8. A witch or a practitioner of voodoo
9. It was found deserted; no trace of the crew was ever discovered
10. Spontaneous combustion
11. Blasphemy
12. Bigfoot
13. Mermaid
14. France
15. They were carved into the turf of chalk hillsides
16. Spiritualism
17. Poltergeist
18. Anne Boleyn
19. Atlantis
20. Levitation
21. Standing Stones
22. A stake through the heart
23. The Holy Grail
24. Jeanne Dixon
25. Haiti

Entertaining Arts   The Small Screen

1. Peter Falk
2. All in the Family
3. Emmy
4. Twin Peaks
5. Antique dealer
6. Lindsay Wagner
7. Jane Seymour
8. All Creatures Great and Small
9. Diana Trent
10. Shari Lewis
11. Farrah Fawcett-Majors
12. Monty Python's Flying Circus
13. Helen Mirren
14. Loretta Swit
15. Ponderosa
16. The Untouchables
17. Uncle and nephew
18. The Raj Quartet
19. Lou Ferrigno
20. Zeb
21. Oprah Winfrey
22. Stephanie Beacham
23. Edward Asner
24. 1960
25. Sue-Ellen, played by Linda Gray

Natural World   Insects and Reptiles

1. Beetle
2. In sand
3. To guard the colony
4. Carapace
5. The tip of the tail
6. To attract mates
7. Wax
8. Gripping the walls of its tunnel as it moves along
9. Coil around it and squeeze
10. Three
11. In water
12. Death in the house
13. A creature without a backbone
14. Caterpillar
15. Poisonous bite
16. On the leaves of mulberry trees
17. Lepidoptera
18. From its antler-like horns
19. Queen, workers and drones
20. By smell
21. Members of the crocodile family
22. Pygmy
23. It hibernates
24. Metamorphosis
25. 'Tasting' the air to smell out other animals

Food and Drink   Healthy Eating

1. Wheat
2. Vitamin D
3. Muesli
4. Textured vegetable protein
5. Milk
6. Tofu
7. Fresh fruit and vegetables
8. To destroy harmful bacteria
9. Amino acids
10. Elimination diet
11. Vitamin A
12. Low-fat cheese
13. Macrobiotic
14. Vitamin C
15. Anorexia nervosa
16. Yeast extract
17. Chocolate
18. Yellow colouring
19. Vitamin A
20. Anaemia
21. Heavy drinking and malnutrition
22. Monosodium glutamate
23. Vitamin B12
24. When sunlight falls on the skin
25. Recommended daily intake

Twentieth Century   The Communist World

1. Truth
2. Alexander Dubcek
3. 1989
4. 1991
5. Commonwealth of Independent States
6. Catholicism
7. Leonid Brezhnev
8. Soviet labour camp
9. 1960s
10. Raisa
11. 1917
12. Riga
13. A human chain from Estonia through Latvia to Lithuania
14. Armenia and Azerbaijan
15. Vodka
16. Nixon
17. Checkpoint Charlie
18. His reforms did not improve the economic situation
19. He landed a small plane in Red Square
20. Ukraine
21. K.G.B
22. Georgia
23. Bulganin
24. Cruise
25. Lech Walesa

Sports and Pastimes   Leisure Time

1. Single lens reflex
2. 15
3. Postcards
4. An early mountain bike
5. Panning
6. It may only move to an adjacent square
7. The curved back end of the board
8. Tiddlywinks
9. Any freshwater fish that is not a member of the salmon family
10. Germany
11. You frighten it away
12. Wedge
13. Dungeons and Dragons
14. Pulling the front wheel into the air and balancing on the back one
15. At a funfair
16. Flysheet
17. Toe clips
18. Ludo
19. Match box labels
20. Cardinal points
21. Bridge and backgammon
22. Archery
23. Bar billiards
24. Finland
25. Loft

Pot Luck

1. The owl
2. Tuberculosis
3. Harold Pinter
4. Salome
5. Stroke
6. Aphrodite
7. The Purple Heart
8. Testosterone
9. The Queen Mother
10. In a car crash
11. Octet
12. 525
13. Plant it
14. Minimum Lending Rate
15. Salvation Army
16. An olive branch
17. Sukiyaki
18. Della Street
19. Badgers
20. Olive trees
21. Goldie Hawn
22. Jane Fonda
23. Greece
24. United Nations
25. John B. Connally

Educational Scientific and Cultural Organization

Quiz

13

1 In which century did Catherine the Great rule in Russia?

2 Which French Queen spent so wildly that she was known as 'Madame Deficit'?

3 Who succeeded Queen Juliana as ruler of the Netherlands in 1980?

4 Which British sovereign had the longest reign?

5 Prince Albert of Liège succeeded to which throne in 1993?

6 Which English Queen was nicknamed Brandy Nan?

7 Which Swedish Queen did Greta Garbo play on screen? ▲

8 Queen Salote reigned from 1918 to 1965 over which island kingdom?

9 In ancient times which country was ruled by the Moguls?

10 In 1931, when Communist forces were strong in his country, Alfonso XIII had to abdicate. What was his country?

11 To which powerful royal house did the Emperors Ferdinand I and Franz Joseph I of Austria belong?

12 Who followed King David as King of Israel?

13 Whom did Queen Elizabeth I succeed to the British throne? ▼

14 What happened to William II, Emperor of Germany, when he was defeated by the Allies in World War I?

15 Where was Napoleon born?

16 Which King of Prussia waged the Seven Years War in the 18th century?

17 How were the English King Richard I and his successor King John related?

18 Boris III was king of which country from 1918 to 1943?

19 Which French king was called Le Roi Soleil?

20 Who was the enlightened King of Sardinia who became King of Italy when the states united in 1861?

21 How many children did Queen Victoria and Prince Albert have?

22 To which royal house did Louis XIV, Henry IV and Louis Philippe of France belong?

23 Name the King of Jordan.

24 Which King of England was the first Prince of Wales?

25 King Umberto was deposed from the throne of which country in 1946?

1 The highest note can be reached by which female voice?

2 Which composer, from an Austrian family of musicians, was known as the 'Waltz King'?

3 In which country was the composer Debussy born?

4 What does the musical term fortissimo mean?

5 Arthur Sullivan wrote the music for the famous Savoy Operas? Who wrote the words?

6 Nijinsky was one of the greatest of all ballet dancers. Why did his career come to a premature end?

7 In which city did jazz have its origins?

8 Musical instruments are divided into four classes. Strings, wind instruments and keyboard are three of them. What is the fourth?

9 Which aria from Puccini's Madame Butterfly has become an 'opera pop song'?

10 At what age did Mozart die? ▲

11 What does the musical term lento mean?

12 Which composer wrote the Emperor Concerto and the Ninth Symphony?

13 Which Tchaikovsky ballet has Princess Aurora as a heroine?

14 A plectrum is used to play which musical instrument?

15 What is a paradiddle?

16 Who wrote the Enigma Variations and The Dream of Gerontius?

17 What were Bach's given names?

18 Which dancer was strangled by her own scarf?

19 Who wrote the opera Gloriana in honour of the coronation of Queen Elizabeth II in 1953?

20 Which ballet uses music by Chopin?

21 In which opera is the heroine a girl who works in a cigarette factory?

22 What nationality was the composer Delius, who died in 1934?

23 How many strings does a violin have?

24 Which ballerina was famous for her solo performance in The Dying Swan (La Cygne)? ▼

25 In which city is the famous opera house, La Scala?

1 What stimulant is found in tea and coffee?

2 Which drink is sometimes called Adam's Ale?

3 What are the ingredients of a Screwdriver? ▲

4 If a wine is described as brut, what does it say about the taste? ▶

5 What is a pre-prandial drink?

6 What is added to coffee to make Caribbean coffee?

7 What is added to coffee to make Kentucky coffee?

8 The organisation CAMRA has branches in many parts of the United Kingdom. What do the initials stand for?

9 For what type of drink was chicory a wartime substitute?

10 A Sidecar contains brandy, lemon juice and which liqueur?

11 Why are bottles that contain beer usually coloured brown?

12 From which fruit is perry made?

13 Malvern and Ashbourne are the best known of Britain's mineral waters. Which of these is sparkling?

14 A fortified wine has grape spirit added to increase the alcoholic strength – to what percentage?

15 What is a firkin?

16 What drink is associated with Holy Island, Northumberland, England?

17 A Piña Colada contains pineapple juice, coconut cream (or Malibu) and what else?

18 What type of wine usually accompanies game?

19 For what reason is yeast introduced into beer making?

20 What, in wine production, is another name for 'marrying'?

21 In which United States city was Coca-Cola originally made?

22 What is a posset?

23 Cradles are often used for serving wine, but what was the original use?

24 What does cuvée mean as a description of wine?

25 Planter's Punch has no set formula but on which spirit is it based?

1. What is the playing time of a Rugby League match?

2. How many intervals does an American football game have?

3. Walter Payton has been called the greatest-ever American football player. What is his nickname?

4. Which was the first British football club to win the European Cup?

5. What is the Argentinean soccer player Maradona's given name?

6. Which is larger, the Canadian or the American football field?

7. In 1990, West Germany won soccer's World Cup. Which team won in 1986?

8. Which country's rugby football team is called the All Blacks? ▼ ▶

9. When footballer Paul Gascoigne transferred from Tottenham Hotspur in 1991-2, the fee was £5.5 million. Where did he transfer to?

10. Which American football coach was known as Papa Bear?

11. Which major sporting event began on 17 June, 1994 at Soldier Field in Chicago?

12. In the sport of soccer, a yellow card shown to a player means a caution. What does a red card actually mean?

13. Where is the home of the American football team, the Cardinals?

14 In American football, how many players from each team join the scrimmage line?

15 Which two teams played the 1993 FA Cup at Wembley?

16 On what shape of pitch is Australian rules football played?

17 Arsenal is the team that has appeared most often in the FA Cup Final. How many times?

18 Which year was the first Olympic Games at which an official football tournament was played?

19 How many substitutes in American football?

20 Which country won the 6th European Football Championship for Women?

21 Mick Luckhurst joined a leading NFL club in the United States and became one of their star players; in 1984 he became their all-time leading scorer. Name his team.

22 Rugby Union has two teams of 15 players; how many players does each team in Rugby League have?

23 Name the German soccer star who led West Germany to victory over Holland in the World Cup, then managed the team that defeated Argentina in 1990.

24 Which country introduced Rugby League in 1990 and sent a 90-man squad on a three-month tour of Britain?

25 Which country kept the Jules Rimet Trophy, the first World Cup trophy, for good in 1970 after winning it three times out of four?

1 Whose autobiography is called Part of My Soul?

2 What is the estimate of the number of Jews who died in the Holocaust?

3 Which racist organization, whose members wear special outfits that conceal their identities, was founded in the South after the American Civil War?

4 The term 'prejudice' is derived from which word?

5 Which racial group did President Idi Amin of Uganda expel from his country in 1972?

6 In South Africa, people were assigned to one of four groups for the purpose of apartheid. They included Europeans, Asiatics and Black Africans. What was the fourth group?

7 What was the other name for 'Bantustans' in South Africa?

8 In what field did Miss Buss and Miss Beale become well-known in Britain in the last century?

9 The civil rights organization known as CORE was founded in the United States in 1942. What do the initials stand for?

10 In which area of London did the race riots of 1981 take place?

11 What name is given to the deliberate destruction of a specific social, national or racial group?

12 The Nazi party began in Germany in 1919. What was its full name?

13 The first slaves arrived in the United States in 1619 but they were imported in large numbers later in the century, mainly to work in what type of plantations?

14 In which decade were schools desegregated in the United States?

15 Who founded the first birth control clinic in England?

16 Nelson Mandela is President of which African organization? ◀

17 Which black woman writer is the author of I Know Why the Caged Bird Sings?

18 Who became the first Prime Minister of Israel in 1948?

19 How did woman's suffrage campaigner Emily Wilding Davison ensure a place in history on Derby Day in 1913? ▶

20 What item of clothing were supporters of Women's Lib supposed to burn?

21 Who was the first woman to run for Vice-President in the United States in 1984?

22 Which Australian author wrote The Female Eunuch?

23 Who was the political leader, later Prime Minister of South Africa, who said 'Natives will be taught from childhood to realize that equality with Europeans is not for them'?

24 In the United States, how many states had granted women the vote before World War I?

25 For which type of women did Erin Pizzey campaign in Britain?

1. If cows are lying down in the field, what weather does this traditionally foretell?

2. What is the name given to a column of swirling dust or soil raised into the air by a small whirl-wind?

3. There are three bands of climate in the world: tropical, polar and which other?

4. What are the long curving lines on a weather map, designating areas of equal pressure, called?

5. What can be cumulus, stratus or lenticular?

6. Which weather system brings cloudy skies, winds and rain?

7. Who was the Norse god of thunder?

8. When there is a thunderstorm, why do you see the lightning before you hear the thunder? ▲

9. What name is given to the mixture of fog and smoke?

10. In which country is the hottest place in the world?

11. Why do metal pipes often burst when the water inside turns to ice?

12. The coasts of which countries experience the strong, dry and cold north westerly wind called the mistral?

13. What shape is a tornado?

14. What does an anemometer measure?

15 Pine cones are often used by amateur weather forecasters. What happens if the weather is about to turn wet?

16 What name is given to the white ice that forms on the branches of trees in very cold weather?

17 How many different patterns of snow flakes are there?

18 Hurricanes cause tremendous damage. What is the ring of low pressure at the centre of the storm called? ▼

19 What can be ribbon, rocket, streak or sheet?

20 An anticyclone brings what type of weather to the area it covers?

21 What name is given to the torrential rains experienced in India for six months beginning in May?

22 Weather occurs in the troposphere where most water vapour exists. Where do airliners fly to avoid too many bumps?

23 The special type of blue-green lightning that clings to the wing tips of most aircraft is known as what?

24 As the old saying goes a red sky at night means 'shepherd's delight', what does a red sky in the morning mean?

25 What do we call the refraction, reflection and dispersal of the suns rays caused by raindrops in the sky?

8 Who was the only man to become Vice President and President without being elected to either post?

9 Who said: 'Read my lips. No new taxes!'?

10 Two Presidents have been assassinated this century. One was Kennedy; who was the other?

11 The 27th President (1900-1913) was the heaviest President of all time. Who was he?

12 Where was Bill Clinton born?

1 Which President was crippled by polio? ▲

2 To what office did John F. Kennedy appoint his younger brother Robert? ▶

3 In 1961, what did Kennedy call on America to achieve in the next decade?

4 About which President did Dorothy Parker, when told of his death, say 'How could they tell?'?

5 Which President began his working life as a sports commentator?

6 Which President withdrew American troops from Vietnam?

7 What was Jimmy Carter's family business?

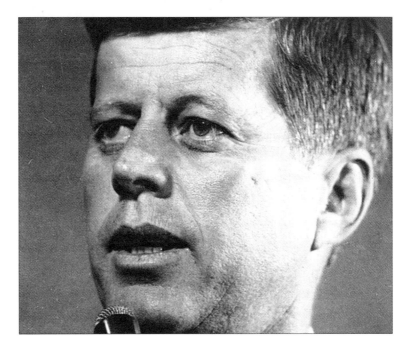

13 Which President renamed 'Shangri-la' as 'Camp David' after his grandson?

14 Who said in his inaugural speech 'The only thing we have to fear is fear itself'?

15 Which President was awarded the Nobel Peace Prize in 1919?

16 The 1981 attempted assassination of Ronald Reagan took place as he left which hotel?

17 'Ask not what your country can do for you...'. Complete this quotation from Kennedy's inaugural address. ▲

18 About what did President Bush say, 'A line has been drawn in the sand'?

19 What was the name given to the economics of the Reagan era?

20 Who was the independent candidate in the 1992 presidential campaign?

21 In a time of rising inflation, who called on Congress to 'bite the bullet'?

22 In Gerald R. Ford's name, what did the initial R. stand for?

23 Which President, early this century, was called the 'Great Engineer' and then later, when his policies failed to work, the 'President Reject'?

24 Which state did Harry S. Truman represent before his elevation?

25 What was the name of President Eisenhower's wife?

1. In which American state is Fort Knox?

2. What is the more usual name for the polygraph?

3. Who is singer Cleo Laine's husband?

4. What is the name for the organism on which a parasite lives and feeds?

5. Who was the first Roman Emperor to convert to Christianity?

6. What is the only movable bone in the human skull?

7. In which country is the Kimberley gold field?

8. What will never make a silk purse?

9. Which world famous poet lived at Dove Cottage ▶ in Grasmere?

10. In the 1993 film, Mrs Doubtfire, who plays the title role?

11. On what type of business was the fortune of John F. Kennedy's family built?

12. Greenland has two official languages. One is Greenlandic; what is the other?

13. What is the distaff side of the family?

14. When is Lammas day?

15. Which company launched the 'Walkman'?

16. What type of acid is in bee stings?

17. In the song, the House of the Rising Sun was in which city?

18. What sport would you be watching if the New York Knickerbockers were playing?

19. What word describes a doctor specializing in the medical problems of old age?

20. If you were making a wiener schnitzel, what meat would you buy?

21. 'The Mindbenders' were the backing group for which pop singer?

22. In the Bible, whom did God tell, 'Escape to the mountain, lest thou be consumed'?

23. Where was Princess Elizabeth when she learned that she had become Queen Elizabeth II?

24. Which country's flag shows a white cross on a red background?

25. If your birthstone is turquoise, which is your birth month?

People and Places   Kings and Queens

1. 18th century
2. Marie Antoinette
3. Queen Beatrix
4. Queen Victoria
5. Belgium
6. Queen Anne
7. Queen Christina
8. Tonga
9. India
10. Spain
11. Hapsburg
12. Solomon
13. Mary I
14. He fled into exile in Holland
15. Corsica
16. Frederick the Great
17. Brothers
18. Bulgaria
19. Louis XIV
20. Victor Emmanuel
21. Nine
22. Bourbon
23. King Hussein
24. Edward II
25. Italy

Entertaining Arts   Music and Dance

1. Soprano
2. Johann Strauss
3. France
4. Very loud
5. W.S. Gilbert
6. He suffered from mental illness
7. New Orleans
8. Percussion
9. One Fine Day
10. 35
11. Slow
12. Ludwig van Beethoven
13. Sleeping Beauty
14. Guitar
15. A drum roll
16. Elgar
17. Johann Sebastian
18. Isadora Duncan
19. Benjamin Britten
20. Les Sylphides
21. Carmen
22. English
23. Four
24. Anna Pavlova
25. Milan

Food and Drink   Drink Up!

1. Caffeine
2. Water
3. Vodka and orange juice
4. It will be very dry
5. An aperitif
6. Rum
7. Southern Comfort
8. Campaign for Real Ale
9. Coffee
10. Cointreau
11. To protect the contents
from harmful sunlight
12. Pears
13. Ashbourne
14. 20 per cent
15. A small barrel or measure of ale
16. Lindisfarne mead
17. White rum
18. Robust red wine
19. To produce fermentation
20. Blending
21. Atlanta, Georgia
22. A drink of milk and ale
23. For bringing wines from the cellar without disturbing the sediment
24. Wine from the contents of a single vat
25. Rum

Sports and Pastimes   Football Facts

1. 80 minutes plus one interval
2. One long and two short
3. Sweetness
4. Celtic
5. Diego
6. Canadian
7. Argentina
8. New Zealand
9. Lazio, Italy
10. George Halas
11. Football World Cup
12. The player is sent off
13. Phoenix, Arizona
14. At least seven
15. Arsenal and Sheffield Wednesday
16. Oval
17. 12
18. 1908
19. An unlimited number
20. Norway
21. Atlanta Falcons
22. 13
23. Franz Beckenbauer
24. Russia
25. Brazil

History   Equal Rights

1. Winnie Mandela
2. 6 million
3. Ku Klux Klan
4. Prejudge
5. Asians
6. Coloureds
7. Homelands
8. Education for girls
9. Congress of Racial Equality
10. Brixton
11. Genocide
12. National Socialist Workers' Party
13. Tobacco and cotton
14. 1950s
15. Marie Stopes
16. African National Congress
17. Maya Angelou
18. David Ben-Gurion
19. She threw herself under the hooves of the leading horse
20. Bra
21. Geraldine Ferraro
22. Germaine Greer
23. Verwoerd
24. 11
25. Battered wives

Natural World   Weather

1. Rain
2. Dust devil
3. Temperate
4. Isobars
5. Clouds
6. Depression
7. Thor
8. Light travels faster than sound
9. Smog
10. Ethiopia
11. Water expands when it
freezes
12. Spain and France
13. Funnel-shaped
14. Wind speed
15. The scales close up
16. Rime or hoarfrost
17. Millions
18. Eye
19. Lightning
20. Settled weather
21. Monsoons
22. The stratosphere
23. St. Elmo's fire
24. Shepherd's warning
25. A rainbow

Twentieth Century   American Presidents

1. Roosevelt
2. Attorney General
3. Land the first man on the moon
4. Calvin Coolidge
5. Ronald Reagan
6. Richard Nixon
7. Wholesale peanut business
8. Gerald Ford
9. George Bush
10. William McKinley
11. William H. Taft
12. Hope, Arkansas
13. Dwight D. Eisenhower
14. Franklin D. Roosevelt
15. Woodrow Wilson
16. Washington Hilton
17. '... ask what you can do for your country'
18. Iraq's invasion of Kuwait
19. Reaganomics
20. Ross Perot
21. Lyndon Johnson
22. Rudolph
23. Herbert Hoover
24. Missouri
25. Mamie

Pot Luck

1. Kentucky
2. Lie detector
3. John Dankworth
4. Host
5. Constantine
6. Mandible or jawbone
7. Western Australia
8. A sow's ear
9. Wordsworth
10. Robin Williams
11. Real estate
12. Danish
13. The female side
14. August 1
15. Sony
16. Formic acid
17. New Orleans
18. Basketball
19. Geriatrician
20. Veal
21. Wayne Fontana
22. Lot
23. Kenya
24. Switzerland
25. December

Quiz

14

1 In which country would you find Legoland?

2 What is the Spanish name for a bullfighter? ▲

3 Which member of the British royal family favoured the holiday island of Mustique?

4 Spain's Costa Brava is a favourite destination of holidaymakers. What does 'Costa Brava' mean?

5 If you were reading Le Monde or Le Figaro with your morning coffee, where would you be?

6 In Israel, you will find that most shops shut during the Shabat or Sabbath. When is this?

7 For which festival, held in July, is the town of Bayreuth in Germany famous?

8 Where would you visit the Colossi of Memnon?

9 Which city was once known as Byzantium and later as Constantinople?

10 What is the name given to a lover of all things French?

11 Neuschwanstein is a romantic fairytale castle perched on a forested mountain in Bavaria. Who was the 'Mad King' who built it? ▶

12 In which country would you find the world's oldest brewery?

13 What is the special name given to an Arab market?

14 On which island is the Blue Grotto a major tourist attraction?

15 Where in the world would you find an eisteddfod?

16 Which Scandinavian country is famous for its fjords?

17 What unit of currency is used in India?

18 Where would you find gondoliers?

19 On which side of the road would you drive in Japan?

20 Which country was once known as Cathay?

21 If you wanted to follow in the footsteps of Count Dracula, you might visit Transylvania. In which country is it?

22 Where would you visit the Keys, Highland Hammocks and Everglades?

23 'The Emerald Isle' is the romantic name for which country?

24 Which great Moorish building in Spain includes the Court of Myrtles, Place of Cisterns, Hall of Ambassadors and the Hall of Secrets?

25 What is the French flag called?

1. Whose schoolmates were Bob Cherry, Frank Nugent and Harry Wharton?

2. In which novel does Catherine Earnshaw fall in love with Heathcliff?

3. What was the name of Long John Silver's parrot in Treasure Island?

4. Sweeney Todd was the demon barber who slit the throats of his customers. What did he do with the bodies?

5. 5. In which children's TV series did the Daleks threaten to 'exterminate' their enemies?

6. Which character did Joan Collins play in Dynasty? ▲

7. In which city does Bruce Wayne live and fight villains as Batman?

8. Gomez, Morticia and Uncle Fester belong to which family?

9. In The Wizard of Oz, which of the characters accompanying Dorothy to see the wizard was seeking a brain?

10. Which bird did the Ancient Mariner kill?

11. Jacob Marley was the partner of which famous miser in A Christmas Carol?

12. Who is constantly chased by Sylvester in cartoons?

13 What was the number of The Prisoner?

14 Which Japanese lady married Lieutenant Pinkerton and committed suicide when he deserted her?

15 Kunta Kinte was the leading figure in which book and TV mini-series?

16 What was the name of Frank Spencer's long-suffering wife in Some Mothers Do 'Ave 'Em?

17 Which American cops were played by Paul Michael Glaser and David Soul?

18 Who was a 'bear of very little brain'?

19 Whose friends are Obelix the muscle-man and Getafix the Druid?

20 Bunny Manders is the side-kick of which upper crust crook?

21 Who is the villain of the Star Wars trilogy?

22 Name M's secretary in the James Bond stories? ▼

23 Which famous frog puppet is the leader of the Muppets?

24 Which famous storyteller told the tales of Brer Rabbit and Brer Fox?

25 Who is the heroine of R.B. Blackmore's novel, the member of an outlaw family who falls in love with John Ridd?

1 Satay is an Asian dish with pieces of meat or fish grilled on bamboo skewers. What type of sauce is usually served with it? ▲

2 What are bratwurst, bockwurst and knackwurst?

3 What is the name given to savoury Indian pasties filled with meat or vegetables and seasoned with herbs and spices?

4 What is the name given to the yeasted bread containing yogurt that is served in Indian restaurants?

5 If you were in an American restaurant and you wanted your food grilled, what description would you look for? ▶

6 Also in an American restaurant, if you were offered 'grits', what would you expect to get?

7 Tahini is a paste used in Middle Eastern cooking. From what is it made?

8 In Japanese cooking, what are little parcels of raw fish and rice called?

9 What is salmagundi?

10 Gumbo is a Creole stew with meat, chicken or seafood, tomatoes and onions and what essential vegetable?

11 What is the main ingredient of the Russian soup bortsch?

12 Biltong originated in South Africa. What exactly is it?

13 Danish open sandwiches are usually called smorrebrod. What is the literal meaning of this word?

14 Couscous comes from North Africa. What is its base?

15 In China, what favourite drink is known as cha or ch'a?

16 Added to Indian dishes at the end of cooking time, what is garam masala?

17 From which country's cuisine does the thick soup called minestrone come?

18 In Spain, what are tapas?

19 What is the name of the dish made in the north of England from pig's blood, fat, oatmeal, onions and spices?

20 Goulash gets its name from the Hungarian word gulgas, meaning shepherd, as shepherds were supposed to have invented it. What is its main spice?

21 On a Russian menu, what is a coulibiac?

22 What are flapjacks?

23 In Italian cooking, what are gnocchi?

24 If pasta is cooked al dente, what does it mean?

25 In France, what is a baguette?

1 In skiing, what is the other name for cross country racing?

2 How many competitors form a team in bobsleigh racing?

3 Katarina Witt has been one of the world's brightest skating stars. Which country did she represent in competition?

4 In ice hockey, what is the 'sin bin'?

5 What is a piste?

6 The Summer Olympics have been held since 1896. In which year was the first Winter Olympics?

7 What name is given to a toboggan with metal runners but no steering or brakes, ridden in a sitting or face-up lying position?

8 In ice skating, what is 'tracing'?

9 What is the crouched position in downhill racing on smooth, straight slopes called?

10 In which country did ice hockey originate?

11 Which two sports make up the biathlon, introduced into the Winter Olympics in 1960?

12 In ski-jumping, what position must the skis maintain until just before landing?

13 Which ice or snow sport was the first to gain Olympic status?

14 What is the Super-G?

15 In skiing, what are aerials?

16 Which ice sport has leads, seconds, thirds and skips?

17 Ice hockey has teams with up to 20 players, but how many can be on the ice at one time?

18 What is the sport of the ski marathon called in the United States?

19 Which country hosted the 1992 Winter Olympics?

20 A slalom is a downhill race through a series of 'gates'. What are the gates represented by ? ◀ ▲

21 In snowboarding, boards are used instead of what?

22 Which country held the first recorded ski race in 1767?

23 What are moguls in skiing?

24 In ski-jumping, a 'large' jump is 85-90 metres. Jumps over 90 metres become a separate event called what?

25 What type of skiing is skijoring?

1 What do the initials VCR stand for?

2 Isaac Pitman published Stenographic Soundhand in 1837. What is his system now known as?

3 Before the telephone was invented, what electrical device was used to send messages?

4 The picture of a small dog listening to 'his master's voice' on a gramophone was the trade mark of which record company?

5 In a computer, what is the CPU?

6 What unit is used to measure the frequency of radio waves? ▲

7 For what are sandwich boards used?

8 What did John Logie Baird invent?

9 In which field of communication were Sir Humphrey Davy and Joseph Niepce involved?

10 Radar played an important part in the conduct of World War II, detecting the position of enemy planes. What does RADAR stand for?

11 What were 'cats' whiskers' used for in early 'crystal' radios?

12 In what year was the first flight around the world over both poles?

13 What was the name of the small box camera which became available early this century?

14 When was The Times first published?

15 What name is given to the decorated books made by monks in the Middle Ages?

16 Why are satellites necessary to send VHF signals around the world?

17 What year was the 'Telstar' satellite launched from Cape Canaveral?

18 Software is the name given to what?

19 Who printed the first book in English in 1474?

20 What is the name given to the method of sending signals by arrangement of flags or a post with movable arms? ▼

21 BASIC is an easy to learn computer language. What do the initials stand for?

22 When Thomas Edison invented the phonograph, the predecessor of the record player, what was the first recording he made?

23 The first records were played at 78 rpm. What does 'rpm' stand for?

24 What name is given to the spreading of opinions and ideas, often by giving one-sided information?

25 What was the first postage stamp called?

1. What name is given to a group of wolves? ▲

2. What do the Californian condor, the giant anteater and the Indian lion have in common?

3. In what position do adult horses normally sleep?

4. On what does the common mole normally feed?

5. What type of animals are eland, kudu and gazelles?

6. What is the collective name for a group of domestic cats?

7. Between which months do the hedgehog and dormouse hibernate?

8. If a rabbit thumps its back feet on the ground, what is it likely to be doing?

9 Why do thousands of Alaskan fur seals go to Pribilof Islands in the Bering Sea each year?

10 What is the fastest land mammal?

11 What is the main food of the aardvark?

12 The baby of which animal is called a joey?

13 The soles of Polar bears' feet differ from those of other bears. In what way?

14 Animals that eat grass are called grazers. What name is given to animals like elephants and giraffes, that eat leaves from trees and bushes?

15 The coypu is an aquatic rodent resembling the beaver. What is it sometimes called?

16 What name is given to the home of the beaver? ▼

17 Which is the largest mammal baby?

18 Which are the only mammals that can fly?

19 Nesting materials are in short supply in the Antarctic. Where do king and emperor penguins lay their eggs?

20 In ancient Egypt, the mongoose was a sacred animal. Families often kept one for what purpose?

21 What is the other name for a Russian wolfhound?

22 Lions live in family groups. What are they called?

23 What is the kangaroo's normal method of defence?

24 What type of animal is the caribou?

25 Which animal has a name that means 'river horse'?

1 1. From which country did the Soviet Union withdraw in 1988, ending a 10-year war?

2 Which engineering project, shared between Britain and France, was opened in December 1993?

3 Who was the first Prime Minister of an independent Zimbabwe?

4 4. In which country did Tamil guerrillas battle for political freedom?

5 5. Who is believed to be the wealthiest man in the world because of oil riches?

6 6. Which two young Australians made their names in Neighbours and then went on to great success on the pop scene?

7 The 1980s was the decade of the 'yuppie'. What does 'yuppie' stand for?

8 What disease killed film star Rock Hudson? ▶

9 Who became the first socialist President of France in 1981 and was re-elected in 1988?

10 The Brady Bill was much in the headlines in the United States in 1993. What did it concern?

11 Who was the President of Argentina when it invaded the Falklands?

12 Name the actor who played Crocodile Dundee.

13 After two years of drought and disorder, President Bush despatched American troops on a humanitarian mission in 'Operation Restore Hope' to which African country?

14 Whom did Neil Kinnock succeed as leader of the Labour party in Britain?

15 The sale of which Van Gogh painting trebled the previous auction price record for a work of art in 1987?

16 Who launched Virgin Airways in 1985?

17 Which American basketball star, reputed to be the world's highest paid sportsman, toured Britain in 1993?

18 Nicolae Ceaucescu, executed in 1989, was dictator of which country?

19 Which British character actor starred in Who Framed Roger Rabbit?

20 Prime Minister Kim Campbell faced a humiliating defeat in the Canadian elections of October 1993. Which party was thrown out of office?

21 Name the Greenpeace ship blown up in New Zealand by French agents on the eve of the protest against French nuclear tests in the Pacific. ◀

22 On which hand does Michael Jackson wear his famous glove?

23 In the attempted assassination of Ronald Reagan, how many people were shot?

24 Dictator Kim II Sung created a godlike status for himself in which country?

25 In 1993 Elton John won a large libel settlement against a British newspaper. What had the newspaper claimed about him?

1 What nationality is golfer Gary Player?

2 Who wrote the novel on which Benjamin Britten based his opera The Turn of the Screw?

3 How many wisdom teeth does the average adult have?

4 The United States has four mainland time zones. Three of them are Pacific, Mountain and Eastern. What is the fourth?

5 Which British racing driver has won most Grand Prix races?

6 What is the name given to the moon that follows the Harvest Moon?

7 On what date is Bastille day celebrated in France?

8 Which country gives a Christmas tree to Britain every year?

9 What race of nomadic people inhabit northern Scandinavia?

10 Which Paris club is famous for the can-can? ▲

11 Who is the patron saint of grave-diggers?

12 The nests from which type of birds are used in birds' nest soup?

13 What was the nickname of the German aviator Baron von Richthofen? ▼

14 British drivers call it a bumper. What do Americans call it?

15 What does white smoke coming from the Vatican chimney mean?

16 According to the proverb, what is nine-tenths of the law?

17 What do we call a chicken when it is under one year old?

18 Who sang Wake up Little Susie, Cathy's Clown and All I have to do is Dream?

19 Who is the young diary writer in the books by Sue Townsend?

20 What was nicknamed the 'Tin Lizzie'?

21 What name is given to the climate that would be produced by nuclear warfare?

22 Which American state was named for the wife of Charles I?

23 In mythology, which nymph was turned into a laurel bush to save her from Apollo?

24 In 1991 Slovenia declared its independence from which country?

25 Which artist angered Henry VIII by painting a flattering portrait of Anne of Cleves?

People and Places   Travel and Tourism

1. Denmark
2. Matador
3. Princess Margaret
4. Rugged coast
5. France
6. From sunset on Friday to sunset on Saturday
7. Wagner festival
8. Near Luxor in Egypt
9. Istanbul
10. Francophile
11. Ludwig II
12. Germany
13. Souk
14. Capri
15. Wales
16. Norway
17. Rupee
18. Venice
19. Left
20. China
21. Romania
22. Florida
23. Ireland
24. The Alhambra, Granada
25. (Drapeau) tricolore

History   Communications

1. Video Cassette Recorder
2. Shorthand
3. Electric telegraph
4. HMV ('His Master's Voice')
5. Central Processing Unit
6. Hertz
7. Advertisements
8. Television
9. Photography
10. Radio Detection And Ranging
11. Tuning
12. 1965
13. Brownie
14. 1785
15. Illuminated manuscripts
16. High frequency radio waves travel in straight lines and cannot follow the curves of the Earth's surface
17. 1962
18. Computer programmes
19. William Caxton
20. Semaphore
21. Beginner's All-purpose Symbolic Instruction Code
22. Mary had a little lamb
23. Revolutions per minute
24. Propaganda

Entertaining Arts   Imaginary Folk

1. Billy Bunter
2. Wuthering Heights
3. Captain Flint
4. Made them into meat pies
5. Dr Who
6. Alexis
7. Gotham City
8. Addams Family
9. Scarecrow
10. Albatross
11. Ebenezer Scrooge
12. Tweety Pie
13. Six
14. Madame Butterfly
15. Roots
16. Betty
17. Starsky and Hutch
18. Winnie-the-Pooh
19. Asterix the Gaul
20. Raffles
21. Darth Vader
22. Miss Moneypenny
23. Kermit
24. Uncle Remus
25. Lorna Doone

Natural World   Animal Life

1. Pack
2. They are all endangered species
3. Standing up
4. Earthworms
5. Antelopes
6. Clowder
7. October and April
8. Warning its fellows of danger
9. To breed
10. Cheetah
11. Termites
12. Kangaroo
13. They are hairy; other bears have naked soles
14. Browsers
15. Swamp Beaver
16. Lodge
17. Blue whale calf
18. Bats
19. On bare ground or ice
20. Keeping down rodents
21. Borzoi
22. Prides
23. It kicks out with powerful back legs
24. Deer
25. Hippopotamus

Food and Drink   International Table

1. Peanut
2. Spicy German sausages
3. Samosas
4. Naan
5. Broiled
6. Coarsely ground grain or beans
7. Ground sesame seeds
8. Sushi
9. An elaborately arranged dish of minced, shredded and sliced salad ingredients, decoratively displayed in contrasting colours
10. Okra
11. Beetroot
12. Dried strips of beef
13. Buttered bread
14. Crushed semolina wheat
15. Tea
16. A mixture of herbs and spices
17. Italy
18. Savoury titbits served with drinks
19. Black pudding
20. Paprika
21. Hot fish pie
22. Pancakes
23. Pasta dumplings
24. Tender but still firm to the bite

Twentieth Century   The 1980s and 1990s

1. Afghanistan
2. Channel Tunnel, Chunnel or Euro Tunnel
3. Robert Mugabe
4. Sri Lanka
5. Sultan of Brunei
6. Kylie Minogue and Jason Donovan
7. Young urban professional
8. AIDS
9. François Mitterand
10. Gun control
11. General Galtieri
12. Paul Hogan
13. Somalia
14. Michael Foot
15. Sunflowers
16. Richard Branson
17. Shaquille O'Neal
18. Romania
19. Bob Hoskins
20. Conservative
21. Rainbow Warrior
22. Right
23. Four
24. North Korea
25. That he was on a bizarre diet

Sports and Pastimes   Ice and Snow Sports

1. Nordic
2. Two or four
3. East Germany
4. The penalty box where players infringing the rules must spend time
5. A downhill ski trail
6. 1924
7. Luge
8. The marks made on the ice by skate blades
9. Egg position
10. Canada
11. Cross-country skiing and rifle shooting
12. Horizontal and parallel
13. Figure skating
14. Super-giant slalom
15. Aerobatic jumps off a ramp
16. Curling
17. Six
18. Citizen racing
19. France
20. Pairs of flagpoles
21. Skis
22. Norway
23. Bumps on a steep slope
24. Ski flying
25. Skiing while being towed

Pot Luck

1. South African
2. Henry James
3. Four
4. Central
5. Jackie Stewart
6. Hunter's Moon
7. July 14
8. Norway
9. Lapps
10. Moulin Rouge
11. St. Anthony
12. Chinese swallows
13. The Red Baron
14. Fender
15. A new pope has been elected
16. Possession
17. Pullet
18. Everley Brothers
19. Adrian Mole
20. Model T Ford
21. Nuclear winter
22. Maryland
23. Daphne
24. Yugoslavia
25. Hans Holbein

Index

Picture Credits:

(Abbreviations Key: r = Right, l = Left, t = Top, c = Centre, b = Below)

BFI: 11, 12, 13, 20, 64, 65, 82, 83, 103, 115, 120, 121, 123, 125, 138, 139, 156, 157, 168, 172, 173, 179, 186, 209, 210, 211, 223, 226, 246, 247, 257. **Mary Evans Picture Library:** 14, 25, 29L, 29R, 32T, 32B, 37, 38, 39, 42, 46, 50, 53, 54, 55, 56, 57BR, 57TL, 69, 71, 91, 92, 93, 105, 108, 109, 110, 111, 119, 122, 136, 141, 145, 155, 158, 159, 162, 165, 180, 181, 187, 191, 198, 199, 200, 201R, 212, 215, 218, 219, 231, 235, 253, 254. **Robert Harding Picture Library:** 15, 16, 17, 51, 132, 176, 177, 178, 213. **Hulton Deutsch Collection:** 10, 18, 19, 22T, 22B, 23, 24, 28, 30, 31, 33, 34, 35, 36, 40, 41, 43, 47, 48, 49, 52, 58, 59, 60, 61TL, 61BR, 68, 70, 74, 75, 76, 77, 78, 79, 84, 85, 86, 87, 88, 89, 90, 96L, 96R, 97, 100, 101, 102, 104, 106, 107, 112, 113, 114, 118, 124, 126, 127, 128, 129, 130, 131, 133, 137, 140, 142, 143, 144, 146, 147, 148, 149, 150, 151, 154, 160, 161, 163, 164; **Syndication International:** 166, 167L, 167R, 169, 174, 175, 182, 183, 184, 185, 190, 193, 194, 195, 196, 197, 201L, 202, 203; **Doug McKenzie:** 204, 205, 208, 214, 216, 217, 220, 221, 222, 227, 228, 229, 230, 232, 233, 234, 236, 237, 238TL, 238BR, 239, 241, 244, 245, 248, 249; **EMPICS LTD:** 250, 251, 251, 255, 256, 258, 259. **Kobal Collection:** 72BL. **Peter Newark's Pictures:** 72TR, 73. 94, 95. **Tate Gallery, London:** 67.

Every effort has been made to trace the copyright holders and we apologise in advance for any unintentional omissions. We would be pleased to insert the appropriate acknowledgement in any subsequent edition of this publication.